LOCOMOTIVE BOILER EXPLOSIONS

Christian H. Hewison, MICE

David & Charles

Publisher's Note

C.H. Hewison's first school was Riber Castle, near Matlock, where the Midland Railway, the rope-worked inclines of the Cromford & High Peak line operated by the London & North Western Railway, the Matlock Cable Tramway, and Bassett-Lowke's exciting catalogues soon attracted his attention, lessons in Latin and Roman History rather losing their impact as a result. After a few years at Lincoln and Pocklington schools he served as a premium apprentice in the LNER's Doncaster Works and then spent some 22 years either managing locomotive depots or at one of the Motive Power Superintendent's head offices, until in 1953 he became a civil servant and joined the Department of Transport's Railway Inspectorate. He was a Member of the Institution of Civil Engineers. Sadly the author died shortly after completing the manuscript, but fortunately his painstaking research into the subject and his experiences with locomotives will be of immense value to the new generations working with steam locomotives on the privately-run tourist steam railways.

British Library Cataloguing in Publication Data
Hewison, Christian H.
    Locomotive boiler explosions.
    I. Title
    625.209

    ISBN 0-7153-8305-1

Typeset by Photo-graphics
and printed in Great Britain
by Redwood Press Ltd, Melksham, Wilts
for David & Charles
Brunel House   Newton Abbot   Devon

Contents

ABBREVIATIONS

RI	The Railway Inspectorate of the Department of Transport
BOT	Board of Trade
DTp	Department of Transport
IO	Inspecting Officer
EI	Employment Inspector
HMSO	Her Majesty's Stationery Office
MSUA	Manchester Steam Users' Association
CME	Chief Mechanical Engineer
BR	British Railways
GWR	Great Western Railway
B&ER	Bristol & Exeter Railway
M&MR	Manchester & Milford Railway
RR	Rhymney Railway
SDR	South Devon Railway
TVR	Taff Vale Railway
LMSR	London Midland & Scottish Railway
CR	Caledonian Railway
G&SWR	Glasgow & South Western Railway
HR	Highland Railway
LNWR	London & North Western Railway
L&YR	Lancashire & Yorkshire Railway
MR	Midland Railway
NLR	North London Railway
WC&ER	Whitehaven, Cleator & Egremont Railway
LNER	London & North Eastern Railway
GCR	Great Central Railway
MS&LR	Manchester, Sheffield & Lincolnshire Railway
SYR	South Yorkshire Railway
GER	Great Eastern Railway
NBR	North British Railway
E&GR	Edinburgh & Glasgow Railway
GNR	Great Northern Railway
GNSR	Great North of Scotland Railway
H&BR	Hull & Barnsley Railway
NER	North Eastern Railway
B&TR	Blyth & Tyne Railway
Y&NMR	York & North Midland Railway
N&CR	Newcastle & Carlisle Railway
SR	Southern Railway
L&SWR	London & South Western Railway
LB&SCR	London, Brighton & South Coast Railway
SE&CR	South Eastern & Chatham Railway
SER	South Eastern Railway
LMS(NCC)	London, Midland & Scottish Railway (Northern Counties Committee)
B&NCR	Belfast & Northern Counties Railway
DW&WR	Dublin, Wicklow & Wexford Railway

Introduction

A locomotive or industrial boiler can be lethal if a defect occurs under steam pressure. The results can vary from a jet of steam and boiler water escaping under pressure to a massive explosion with effects like a bomb. Fortunately today, with modern material testing, proper maintenance and handling, and stringent examination, boiler explosions are rare indeed, but in the early days of railways if they were not common they occurred all too frequently. Even in the last two decades of steam on BR after the second world war there were several major boiler failures.

This book surveys the history of locomotive boiler explosions, and shows the somewhat alarming way in which the pioneer railways, engine builders and the inspecting officers of the Board of Trade in the last century gradually built up their knowledge of the behaviour of high pressure steam boilers and the materials used in their construction. It is an account not previously presented comprehensively in book form. Most of the explosions happened to engines having boiler barrels and firebox casings of iron, and before maintenance schedules had been properly developed. Some were on small railways possessing limited workshop facilities and others occurred on railways whose directors and managers either put profits and large dividends before boiler renewals and deliberately took risks, rather more so with goods engines, or were so short of resources that they felt compelled sometimes to work engines with boilers in a condition that was no longer within the limits that ensured safety. Explosions became less frequent in proportion to the number of engines at work as locomotive engineering improved.

It is not my intention to discourage any of the hundreds of enthusiasts for whom the working of steam-hauled trains on preserved railways and at steam centres has become a delightful and enchanting pastime. A boiler will always be safe as long as the barrel and firebox, together with their stays, are maintained in good condition and the safety valves are kept in order; in addition the steam-carrying pipes and fittings in the cab must not be neglected and an engine must be worked only by competent and approved staff. It is doubtful whether any engines that survive still have boilers with lap joints, except perhaps a few in the National Railway Museum that are too old to be considered for steaming. It should never be forgotten, however, by steam operators, professional or amateur, that boiler explosions are not fortuitous, arising from influences beyond human control, and also that insurance in no way prevents or guards against accidents involving steam under pressure; safe operation of steam locomotives depends on adequate maintenance and proper management. A Guidance Note called *Locomotive Boilers*, available from the Health & Safety Executive, offers excellent counsel.

Brentwood, Essex   C.H. Hewison

CHAPTER I

An Essay on Boilers

The gravest misfortunes that have befallen steam locomotives are derailments, collisions and boiler explosions, and of these the last-named are probably the most awesome. Locomotive boilers have given way under steam pressure from time to time in the British Isles since the first railway engine was put onto the rails; the accidents rarely killed or injured passengers, but in most cases the footplate staff were far less fortunate. This book attempts to review the whole story of boiler explosions on railways in the British Isles, accidents that should never have happened.

It is quite impossible to produce a comprehensive and complete history of all the explosions that have occurred. The earliest railway systems were local ventures regarded by most people as curiosities and of little interest to the national press; if an engine blew up the incident was seen as no more than just another industrial accident, to be mentioned perhaps by some small provincial paper or not chronicled at all. It was only on the creation of the Board of Trade's Railway Inspectorate in 1840 that there was any official reporting by the railway companies of burst boilers and even then full declaration did not become compulsory by law until 1871. The 1842 Regulation of Railways Act required only accidents 'attended with serious personal injury to the public' to be reported. In 1871 another Regulation of Railways Act repealed this and required notification of every accident 'of a kind as to have caused or to be likely to cause loss of life or personal injury, and which may be specified ... by any order to be made ... by the Board of Trade'. Boiler explosions obviously came within this definition, but a Statutory Order issued in 1895 removed any doubt by ruling that the bursting of a boiler was a reportable accident.

Painstaking researches amongst early local newspaper files might bring to light a few accounts of the first locomotive boiler explosions, but until someone undertakes a massive task of study in this field the sources of accounts of boiler failures must be official records and historical books. The Records kept from 1840 onwards by the RI and preserved by the DTp, of which the RI is a Division, have provided the greater part of the accounts in the following pages; the author is grateful to the Chief Inspecting Officer of Railways and to HMSO for giving facilities to study and copy from them.

There are, however, gaps in these official records, most of the incidents contained in them being only those into which there were Public Inquiries; a list compiled by the Manchester Steam Users' Association and published on page 487 of *Engineering* in 1882 includes some 25 cases of locomotive boiler explosions that either did not appear to the RI to merit investigation or, much more likely, were not brought to the RI's notice at all. How many explosions were not notified to the RI must for ever remain unknown and it cannot be certain that after 1871 reports were received from the railways on every case. It is not improbable that now and then railway managers decided to keep quiet about boiler incidents that might perhaps have tended to discourage passengers and frighten the public generally!

The Manchester Steam Users' Association was formed in 1854 when the great era of the mill and factory steam engine was developing. In the first half of the 19th Century many stationary steam boilers were of poor design and crudely built by blacksmiths in possession of little theoretical training, while factory managers and engineers, themselves often rough and unlettered men, hardly understood what boilers needed in the way of maintenance. At that period there were no handbooks or manuals to guide them. The outcome, as more and more plants were installed to provide power for Britain's expanding industrial development, was that calamitous and horrific boiler explosions, frequently causing terrible damage and much loss of life, became alarmingly common. This led to mill owners in the Manchester area becoming interested in the idea of forming an organisation for the periodical examination of boilers and the submission of reports on their condition. A committee was appointed whose members in turn formed an inspecting organisation, naming it the MSUA. The functions of the Association were to examine stationary boilers at regular intervals and to advise on any measures needed to keep them in safe working order, and to test stationary steam engines by taking indicator diagrams and then suggest means of obtaining fuel economy. The mill owners maintained the MSUA by subscriptions; the MSUA engaged a chief inspector and two assistants, who went to work in April 1855.

During the years that followed the MSUA expanded as an ever-increasing number of firms running steam powered plant became subscribers, and its engineers did much valuable and preventive work; in the 1860s an insurance scheme was introduced for its members. By the turn of the century the status of the Association was such that similar boiler inspecting concerns in many parts of the world were seeking advice from its engineers and officers. In 1932 the Association became merged with the British Engine Insurance Company, to whose Principals the author is indebted for these details.

Sad to say, although the MSUA researches were extended to locomotive boilers, and although firms employing works, mine and quarry shunting engines took advantage of the inspection services, the main line railway engineers and the RI more or less ignored the Association. MSUA representatives generally found that they were unwelcome on the railway companies' lines and according to L.E. Fletcher, who was for a long time the Association's chief inspector, whenever he or his colleagues would have liked to examine a main line railway's locomotive boiler that had burst they were usually refused any facilities for doing so. In only one case, as far as the records go, did the RI co-operate with the MSUA, which was at the inquiry into the explosion, to be described later, on the Dublin, Wicklow & Wexford Railway in 1872. Had the railway companies' locomotive superintendents collaborated with the MSUA and taken advantage of its researches and discoveries, instead of assuming that they knew better than anyone else, the explosions on the railways might well have been much fewer than they were.

What, exactly, is an explosion? The severity of a boiler's failure can vary between a bad leak releasing a gush of steam and a boiler's sudden and utter disintegration. A perforation in a flue tube will certainly pour a dangerous amount of high temperature steam into an engine cab but hardly amounts to an explosion. Newspapers are apt to exaggerate, and the press has sometimes described a leak from a punctured flue tube or a broken water gauge glass as a terrible explosion. A few railway history books mention explosions that the DTp and MSUA records do not contain and which may perhaps be inflated versions of relatively minor steam discharges. For practical purposes it can be said that if some part of a boiler gives way, releasing the entire contents instantaneously or almost so, an explosion occurs, but a legal definition of a boiler explosion has been drafted which is:

> The sudden and violent rending of the plant by force of internal steam or fluid pressure (other than pressure of ignited flue gases) causing bodily displacement of any part of the plant together with forcible ejectment of the contents.

Lawyers sometimes reveal remarkable ways of expressing things.

The explosions of locomotive boilers documented by the RI and MSUA, together with three that occurred before 1840, total 137. A few cases in the MSUA list have occurred on colliery or works lines but they have been included because the locomotives concerned may have belonged to a railway company, the list being only a summary and omitting to say whether this was so or not. Apart from these incidents, this book's review does not extend to the hundreds of 'industrial' engines that have been owned and worked by colliery, gas and factory undertakings. Explosions of boilers on such engines doubtless happened, particularly those of early types bought secondhand from the railway companies. A specialised industry grew up as the steam era progressed, devoted to the construction of industrial locomotives that were turned-out with high standards of safety, and explosions amongst them have probably been rare.

Leaving aside all accidents that might rupture a boiler, such as train collisions, impacts by broken connecting rods, wartime bomb or shell damage, there are three possible causes of an explosion. One is the weakening of a boiler by deterioration until it can no longer withstand the normal internal working pressure for which it was designed. The second is the failure of the safety-valves to release excess steam, due to a defect or maladjustment. Finally, there is the collapse of the firebox under steam pressure when the fire has softened the metal because of insufficient water in the boiler. In the event of a boiler barrel bursting, the engine weather board or cab may afford a degree of protection to men on the footplate, who in many such instances have escaped with minor injuries or even none at all, paraticularly in the earlier years of moderate steam pressures and relatively small boilers, but when a firebox suddenly gives way the footplate men's chances of escape or survival are slight.

The earliest stationary engines, designed by Newcomen and other pioneers, worked on the 'atmospheric' system and took steam at pressures of only two or three lb/sq in; their boilers could be made of thin wrought-iron sheets or of cast-iron and usually functioned without much risk. By the end of the eighteenth century inventors were finding that engines driven directly by steam under pressure produced more power, the first successful pressure boiler having apparently been made by Richard Trevithick in or about 1805 in the form of a cylindrical cast-iron vessel with a wrought-iron plate bolted onto its open end. The next step towards making a boiler that could contain steam under a fair pressure was by riveting together iron plates of adequate thickness, and the first locomotive boilers were in this form.

The iron plates that were available to begin with were small, hand beating or rolling by primitive means being the only known methods of manufacture, and many plates were needed to make a boiler. By the late 1830s ironmasters were able to roll plates that were narrow but of good length, enabling the Liverpool & Manchester Railway to introduce boiler barrels built of only four plates, each about 8ft by 3ft, and needing only four longitudinal seams of which at least two were below the water line. This type of construction may have had a technical name but throughout this book it is called the 'long plate' design. It became possible during the 1840s to construct rings for boilers, plates of sufficient size by then being obtainable.

Safety-valves of the 'steelyard' type, having a weighted lever that holds the valve on its seat were, from the beginning, found ideal for stationary boilers and the earliest locomotives were fitted with them. The pressure needed to lift the valve was easily calculated, and up to the opening of the Liverpool & Manchester Railway in 1830 locomotive pressures were usually within 50 lb/sq in.

Early cylindrical factory boilers had a large internal tube from end to end, one extremity containing the fire and the other leading to a chimney; sometimes the tube ran the length of the boiler, turned round and came back, doubling the heating surface. Locomotives followed this one-tube design until in 1829 George Stephenson produced *Rocket* with its multi-tubular boiler and a square chamber for the fire, called the 'firebox'. The next development was to put the firebox inside the boiler, and Stephenson's *Planet* of 1830 appears to have been the first engine with this arrangement, so establishing a standard form that was to be maintained for the next 120 years.

Considerable difficulty was experienced in working early locomotives because of water that the steam carried with it into the cylinders, a handicap called priming. In about 1840 designers gave their firebox casings a vaulted or domed roof, producing what were respectively called 'Gothic' or 'Haystack' boilers. The regulator valve, through which the steam passed into the main steam pipe and usually of the rotating disc type with two sector-shaped openings, was placed in the vault or dome as high above the boiler's water level as it would go, to keep the priming to a minimum. An alternative, devised at about the same time, was to put the regulator valve inside a tall steam dome mounted on the boiler barrel. By about 1855 engines and their boilers had reached the form though not the size that they were to follow until the end of the steam locomotive era.

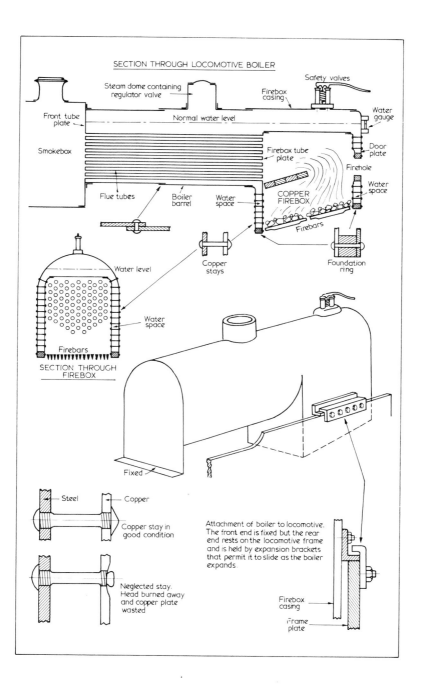

SECTION THROUGH LOCOMOTIVE BOILER

Safety valves

Steam dome containing
regulator valve

Firebox
casing

Water
gauge

Front tube
plate

Normal water level

Door
plate

Smokebox

Firebox tube
plate

Firehole

Water
space

Flue tubes

Boiler
barrel

Water
space

COPPER
FIREBOX

Firebars

Copper
stays

Foundation
ring

Water level

Water
space

Firebars

SECTION THROUGH
FIREBOX

Fixed

Steel

Copper

Copper stay in
good condition

Attachment of boiler to locomotive.
The front end is fixed but the rear
end rests on the locomotive frame
and is held by expansion brackets
that permit it to slide as the boiler
expands.

Neglected stay.
Head burned away
and copper plate
wasted

Firebox
casing

Frame
plate

During the 1830s the steam pressures permitted in locomotive boilers gradually rose. The Jenny Lind class of engine
which appeared in 1847 worked at 120 lb/sq in; by 1865 the
LNWR and MR had express passenger engines running at 150
lb/sq in, and working pressures of 180 to 200 lb/sq in were
reached by the end of the century. Until about 1880 locomotive boiler barrels and firebox casings continued to be of
iron. After Bessemer introduced his process in 1856 steel
began to be used, although its universal adoption was slow as
it was found to pit badly, locomotive engineers preferring to
wait until its superiority in quality was established. The
LNWR apparently pioneered the general introduction of the
steel boiler.

The ordinary modern locomotive boiler (Fig 1) is a barrel
made of steel sheets, the front end being closed by a steel disc
called a tube plate. The lower part of the barrel's rear is
opened-out to form the sides of the firebox casing; the front of
this casing is known as the throat plate and the back is the
doorplate containing a doorway usually called the firehole. In
British locomotive practice the firebox, rectangular and
containing the grate, is invariably of copper and is secured
within the casing, on all four sides, by a large number of short
horizontal rods called stays; the front of the firebox serves as
the boiler's rear tubeplate which the flue tubes connect to the
front tube plate. There is a water space, usually of about four
inches, between the casing and each of the firebox's four sides;
these spaces are sealed at the bottom by a steel 'foundation
ring' which is secured between the firebox and the casing by
rivets that pass horizontally through all three. A boiler must
be worked so that the water not only surrounds the firebox but
also lies several inches deep on the flat firebox roof.

There are two methods of supporting a copper firebox roof,
or crown sheet, depending on the boiler's design. An older
type of engine having a firebox beneath a rounded casing has
some eight to ten roof girders (Fig 2) running longitudinally
about four inches apart across the crown, to which they are
attached by bolts or studs. The girders stiffen the roof so that
it will not deflect downwards under steam pressure and are
kept upright by links suspended from beneath the curved

outer casing; copper's coefficient of expansion being twice that of iron or steel, the holes in the links are slotted so that when the boiler is steamed and expands the firebox may rise freely within the casing by ¼in or so.

The more modern boiler having a casing with a flat top, from which the firebox crown is suspended by roof stays of steel with nuts at each end and spaced about four inches apart, does not need heavy roof girders. The design was introduced in or about 1860 by Alfred Belpaire when he was chief mechanical engineer of the Belgian State Railway. Belpaire boilers gradually became popular and have been adopted all over the world, although not exclusively, because round top casings are cheaper to construct. They were first introduced into Britain by the MS&LR in 1891 although some British railways never used the design. Sir Nigel Gresley, for instance, clung to the round top but suspended the fireboxes of his Pacifics by steel roof stays, those in the centre being of considerable length.

A boiler's copper side stays, also spaced about four inches apart, are threaded at each end and screwed into both plates, projecting slightly through them; these extremities are hammered down to form flat conical heads (Fig 1). In the firebox the heat tends to erode the edges of these heads and the maintenance boilersmiths must from time to time re-hammer the stay ends until the heads again bear firmly on the copper plate; neglect of this attention will allow the fire to act on the plate where it lies beneath the heads, scouring it away.

On early boilers the iron plates were connected by riveted lap joints (Fig 2) but in later years the lap seam was superseded by the butt joint, for reasons that will appear later, and engineers learned that it was necessary to position their longitudinal seams above the boiler's normal water level.

Boilers on the earliest locomotives were replenished by hand-operated force pumps, but before long it became the practice to fit a pair of pumps, each reciprocated by an eccentric on one of the axles, by a connecting rod attached to one of the valve gear eccentrics, or by one of the crossheads. George Stephenson favoured short-stroke pumps worked by eccentrics; Sir Daniel Gooch preferred crosshead-driven

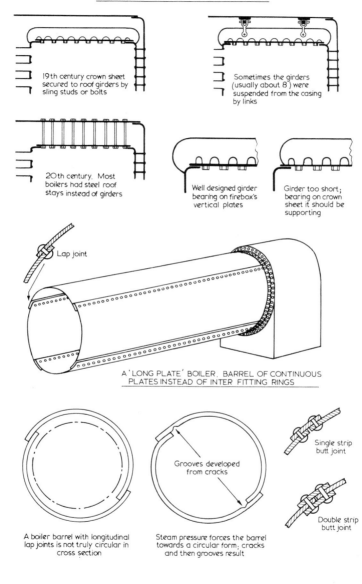

METHODS OF SUPPORTING CROWN SHEETS

19th century crown sheet secured to roof girders by sling studs or bolts

Sometimes the girders (usually about 8") were suspended from the casing by links

20th century. Most boilers had steel roof stays instead of girders

Well designed girder bearing on firebox's vertical plates

Girder too short; bearing on crown sheet it should be supporting

Lap joint

A 'LONG PLATE' BOILER, BARREL OF CONTINUOUS PLATES INSTEAD OF INTER FITTING RINGS

Grooves developed from cracks

Single strip butt joint

Double strip butt joint

A boiler barrel with longitudinal lap joints is not truly circular in cross section

Steam pressure forces the barrel towards a circular form; cracks and then grooves result pumps. In theory either system was ideal, as the pumps injected water in quantities that were fairly proportional to the distance the engine travelled; they worked continuously, however, and the enginemen had to regulate the water delivery from the tender or engine tank by means of cocks on the feed pipes. Branch pipes of small bore leading from the feed terminated in pet cocks that enabled the enginemen to check whether their pumps were working properly. If an engine stood idle for lengthy periods the driver had either to run it up and down a siding several times in order to refill the boiler or sometimes he could oil the rails, apply the hand brake and then let the driving wheels revolve by slipping on the track. Crosshead pumps were troublesome at times; they had to work either with the same stroke as the crosshead itself or with short but sharp strokes as a lug on the crosshead struck alternate collars on the pump rod, and when the engine was running at speed such pumps or their feed connections were liable to burst. A few engines were equipped with steam-driven 'donkey pumps' that the driver could operate at will. All these clumsy water feed arrangements soon vanished when the injector, invented by H.J. Giffard in 1859, was introduced.

Safety-valves are usually fitted towards the rear of a locomotive boiler, which is where most of the steam is made. Weights were soon found unsuitable for the control of locomotive safety-valve levers, being liable to bounce up and down, and spring-balance weighing appliances began to be used instead. The spring balance, fitted vertically with its lower end anchored to the boiler, held down the lever's extremity. When the lever rose as the steam pressure pushed the valve up the spring either stretched or was compressed, depending on the way the balance was assembled. A screw-threaded spindle on the balance's upper end projected up through an eyehole in the lever, and a wing nut or knurled handwheel on the spindle enabled the spring's loading to be adjusted so that the valve opened only when the required working pressure was reached. The lever proportions were usually arranged so that one lb/sq in of steam pressure was balanced by one lb of spring loading or thereabouts.

An LNER boilersmith at work. This company never experienced an explosion in one of its engine boilers. (*Author*)

The first spring balance to be made in Britain was constructed in or about 1770 by Richard Salter who was a spring maker in West Bromwich and one of the pioneer industrialists of the Midlands. He and two of his nephews, John and George, founded the firm of George Salter & Co which has been making springs and balances ever since; Salter weighing machines are commonplace all over the world. The firm patented the spring balance in 1838 and locomotive safety-valve assemblies that incorporated them became known as 'Salter's patent balance valves' or in due course just 'balance valves'. There can be little doubt that balances for safety-valves, which had a pointer in front of a scale so that the boiler's blowing-off pressure could be seen from the footplate, were supplied to the railways by Salter & Co.

These safety-valves were not, unfortunately, immune to interference by enginemen. If an engine stalled when hauling a long string of wagons up a gradient it became much easier to increase the boiler pressure temporarily than to divide the train and take half the wagons up the hill at a time. The men could either screw down the wing nut, and sometimes did so until the valve would not open at all, or they could hang a wagon coupling over the lever. Trainmen worked long hours in the early days of railways and a little unofficial increase in the boiler pressure might well have enabled them to get home earlier. To prevent such tampering, ferrules were sometimes fitted onto the spindles, below the levers, so that the wing nuts could not be screwed down to excess.

It was to prevent tampering by enginemen that John Ramsbottom of the LNWR devised his famous safety-valve at Crewe and produced it in or shortly before 1856. His design employs two valves of equal size and in the form of inverted cones. A horizontal steel lever (iron originally) has two pointed projections, one of which rests in each conical valve, and a coil spring holds down the lever, keeping both valves on their seats—as soon as the steam pressure begins to exceed the permitted maximum it lifts open the valves against the spring's tension. The end of the lever projects back to within the enginemen's reach, which enables them to test the valves by raising the lever to open the rear valve and depressing it to let the front valve lift.

Ramsbottom produced four designs, one of which is not very practical as it has a volute coil spring in compression that is squeezed by the steam pressure; rust could well stick some of the coils together and hinder the opening of the valves. The design having two pillars with a valve in each proved the best and was employed widely until the Ross Pop safety-valve, which needs less headroom, began to supersede it, although not exclusively. Not all the railways adopted Ramsbottom's design, some continuing to use spring-balance valves until well into the twentieth century. Ramsbottom's arrangement avoided the use of wing nuts and was thus secure from risk of interference by enginemen, while a suitable casing prevented weights such as wagon couplings from being put across the lever. It is said that a few drivers tried to defeat the design's aims by pouring lead shot into the inverted cones at times when the engine was not in steam and, by lifting and then depressing the lever, letting the pellets get beneath the projections; if they ever succeeded in doing this it is doubtful whether their actions increased the load on the coil spring by

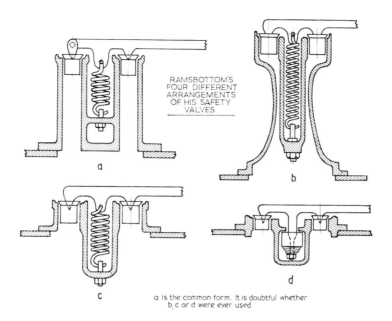

RAMSBOTTOM'S
FOUR DIFFERENT
ARRANGEMENTS
OF HIS SAFETY
VALVES

a

b

c

d

a is the common form. It is doubtful whether
b, c or d were ever used

amounts of any consequence.

Ramsbottom's original designs do not appear to have included the safety links which soon became standard additions. Presumably the need for them was discovered on the first occasion when a coil spring broke and the steam blew the valves and their lever into the sky. These links contain slotted holes and do not impose any load on the valves additional to that of the coil spring, but will retain the equipment should the spring snap.

Many of the railways that clung to the spring-balance type of safety-valve fitted two valves, one immediately in front of the footplate and the other further forward along the boiler barrel where the enginemen could not each it readily. This latter valve was often set to blow-off at a slightly higher pressure than the other, its lever being secured on its screwed spindle by a nut and lock instead of a wing nut, to prevent drivers from dabbling with it; such valves came to be known as 'lock' or 'lock up' valves.

It has been the practice for a long time that every locomotive boiler has two water gauges. The vertical glass tube water gauge is well known and most locomotives had a pair of them, fitted onto the boiler's rear end, above the firehole. The tube is connected at each end to the interior of the boiler by a pair of brass mountings so that the water stands inside it at the same height as that in the boiler itself. It is usually placed so that when the water is only just visible in the tube there are two to three inches of water on the firebox's crown sheet, with the engine standing on a level track. Firemen normally keep the water level about an inch from the top of the visible part of the gauge glass; risks of priming begin to arise if it is allowed any higher.

There is another type of gauge in the form of three 'try' cocks on the boiler's doorplate, positioned about three inches apart and above one another; when the water level is correct, steam will come out of the top cock, water and steam out of the second while only water will be released from the lowermost cock. The jets from the cocks are very small—they are not easy to read because the hot water flashes into steam the moment it reaches the air, while they are very difficult to read or judge by hearing in the dark. Some engines have had one glass tube gauge and one set of try cocks, the Great Eastern being one of the railways that equipped its locomotives in this way.

A glass tube gauge's two mountings each have a shut-off cock, and the lower mounting has a drain cock as well. It is of vital importance that the passages through the two mountings into the boiler are completely unobstructed; if perchance the upper passage becomes stopped by scale or dirt the steam pressure will push the water in the tube to a height above that of the water in the boiler, leading the fireman to believe that he has more water in the boiler than is actually there. The passages are easily tested when the boiler is in steam; if the lower cock is closed and the drain cock opened the steam will or should blow through the upper passage. Closing the upper cock and opening the lower one will likewise test the lower passage. The general arrangement is for the handles of the shut-off cocks to be pointing upwards or downwards when the cocks are open, and for the drain cock handle to be in line with the water passage when in the open position. Both shut-off

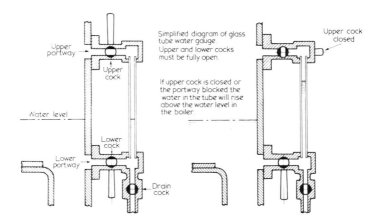

Simplified diagram of glass tube water gauge.
Upper and lower cocks must be fully open.

If upper cock is closed or the portway blocked the water in the tube will rise above the water level in the boiler.

Upper portway

Upper cock

Water level

Lower cock

Lower portway

Drain cock

Upper cock closed

cocks must be kept fully open when the boiler is in steam.

All locomotive fireboxes have, or certainly ought to have, 'low water alarms' in the form of fusible plugs screwed into the crown sheet from below; there are generally two plugs, or sometimes three. The plug is of brass and projects about an inch above the crown sheet. It contains a hole ¼in or so in diameter which is filled tightly with lead, and in the event of the boiler water level falling until the top of the plug is no longer covered the heat of the fire will melt the lead and release a jet of steam into the firebox which should serve to warn the men on the footplate that the water level has become dangerously low, giving them time to act appropriately.

A long time elapsed after the first steam engine went into action before a reliable pressure gauge became available. James Watt designed a gauge consisting of a cylinder containing a piston that steam pressed against the resistance of a spring, but in practice it was unreliable as it proved difficult to keep the piston steamtight. Then someone tried a gauge with a spring-steel diaphragm which, when deflected by an amount proportional to the boiler pressure, moved a lever that in turn revolved a pointer around a dial—unfortunately the steel diaphragm soon rusted. The more modern Schaffer gauge has a horizontal stainless steel diaphragm which, when deflected by steam pressure beneath it, pushes up a rod and so turns a pointer, but it is the Bourdon gauge that has become almost universal. Eugène Bourdon was a French inventor, born in

1808, and the story goes that he had the task of restoring the true shape of a coiled metal pipe that had become flattened by accident. After closing the pipe at one end he then forced water into it; he noticed, however, that the flattened pipe uncoiled slightly under the hyraulic pressure and it occurred to him that here was a principle on which a pressure gauge might work. This may be a legend similar to that of James Watt and the tea kettle, but Bourdon devised a gauge containing a tube of oval cross-section that was bent into a circle or part circle; steam pressure within the tube caused it to open out, moving a rack that revolved a spindle carrying a needle or pointer.

Not every locomotive in the earlier days had a pressure gauge even when they had become available, except the pointer and scale of the spring-balance safety-valve, from which all that an engineman learned was the presure in the boiler when the safety-valves opened. Drivers of the 1850s or so were not particularly discomforted by the lack of pressure gauges; all they asked for was the maximum boiler pressure that their firemen could produce, and they were soon able to detect any drop in pressure when hauling a train. There was a tendency for locomotives to be over-fired so that the safety-valves blew-off all the time the trains were running. The drivers then knew that they had the full working pressure in their boilers, but the practice was most wasteful of fuel.

It is most unlikely that the blacksmiths who riveted the plates for the early locomotive boilers applied any mathematics to their design work to begin with or knew how to do so. However, the basic calculations for the planning of a boiler are fairly simple. To work out the thickness of the plate required to form the barrel we can do all the arithmetic on a one foot slice (Fig 5) since what is true for a foot it true for any length. Suppose a boiler is to have an inside diameter of four feet and is to work at a maximum pressure of 200 lb/sq in. The steam pressure will try to break the slice or ring at two places, AB and CD, and the pressure on each semi-circular half is exactly the same as on the rectangle ABCD. The area of ABCD is 4 sq ft or 576 sq in, and the total pressure on this area at 200 lb/sq in will be 115,200 lb. Ordinary steel, of which all boilers have been made for the last 100 years, breaks in direct tension when submitted to about 30 ton/sq in, but the safety factor allowed by engineers is usually 1 in 6 for steelwork and so all tensile stress is limited to 5 ton/sq in, or 11,200 lb. Our slice of boiler therefore requires 115,200 ÷ 11,200 square inches of steel at sections AB and CD, which is 10.3, or would do if the ring was seamless. In practice it will contain a riveted joint which must be allowed for since this will be the weakest place; a double riveted joint's strength is about 78% that of a solid plate so our 10.3 sq ins becomes 10.3 × 100 ÷ 78 which equals 13.2 or 6.6 sq in at AB alone. AB is 12 in long so its thickness will need to be 6.6 ÷ 12 which equals 0.55 or $\frac{9}{16}$ in.

A boiler draughtsman would make a further adjustment, by increasing the plate's $\frac{9}{16}$ in dimension slightly to allow for losses in thickness likely to be caused by gradual and unavoidable corrosion; he must not overdo this as any such enlargements would add to the locomotive's weight but $\frac{9}{16}$ in would probably be raised to $\frac{5}{8}$ in or perhaps $\frac{11}{16}$ in.

Now we must see whether our four-foot boiler to be built of, say, $\frac{5}{8}$ in plates is likely to get its end blown off. At 4ft diameter the end's area is 12.6 sq ft or 1,810 sq in; at 200 lb/sq in the steam pressure imposes on this area a load of 361,911 lb or 161.5 tons. The area of the steel in the barrel's cross-section in square inches is $48\frac{5}{8}$ (the mean diameter) × 3.1416 × $\frac{5}{8}$ (plate thickness) which amounts to 95.475; we will halve the 95.475 to allow for the riveted joint where the end is attached to the barrel and say 47 sq in. A tensile load of 161.5 tons on 47 sq in amounts to 3.5 ton/sq in; this is well below the 5 ton/sq in permitted maximum, but the actual load will be only about two thirds of this as the flue tubes will occupy about a third of the tube plate's area.

Next, we must test the firebox sides and top by arithmetic. If the stays have a diameter of one inch and are spaced four inches apart, each stay holds 16sq in of steel plate in position and, at its other end, the same area of copper plate. At 200 lb/sq in 16 sq in carry a load of 3,200 lb or 1.43 tons. A one-inch diameter stay has a cross-sectional area of 0.785 sq in, on which 1.43 tons represents just under two ton/sq in,

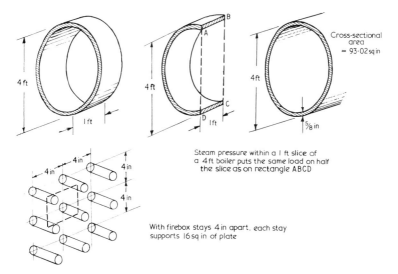

Cross-sectional area = 93·02 sq in

Steam pressure within a 1 ft slice of a 4 ft boiler puts the same load on half the slice as on rectangle ABCD

With firebox stays 4 in apart, each stay supports 16 sq in of plate

and that is only about an eighth of the maximum tension that good copper can withstand—plenty of margin there.

Are readers wondering why so many details have been given about locomotive boilers? Let us now browse through the DTp and MSUA records when the reasons will then be revealed. We shall see that over a period of 122 years hardly any of the principal railway systems in the British Isles managed to avoid at least one boiler explosion, but the numbers of incidents need to be considered in relation to the total number of steam locomotives worked by British and Irish railway companies. The table on page 142, based on returns of rolling stock rendered by the railways to the Railway Inspectorate, shows that between 1860 and 1910 the total rose from 5,801 to 22,640.

The names of the larger companies have been indicated by their initials—GWR, LNWR and so on—on the assumption that readers will already be acquainted with them, but an explanation of the initials is given on page 4. Names less readily known are in full.

All the goods engines that are mentioned in the pages that follow were of the ordinary six-coupled inside-cylinder tender type, except where it is stated that the type remains unknown or a different type is described.

CHAPTER 2

From the Beginning to 1850

What was probably the earliest locomotive boiler explosion, and certainly the most destructive in terms of human life, occurred on 31 July 1815 at Philadelphia, Co Durham, when a very unorthodox railway engine called Brunton's Mechanical Traveller blew-up on the Newbottle Waggonway. The engine had a boiler on four wheels but its two horizontal cylinders and pistons worked levers with 'feet' that acted on the ground between the rails, pushing the engine along. Sixteen people were killed and about 40 injured; presumably most of them were curious sightseers who were standing around the locomotive when the boiler gave way.

On the Stockton & Darlington Railway the boiler of Engine No 5 blew up on 19 March 1828 at Simpasture, a mile or two east of Shildon. According to R. Young's *Timothy Hackworth and the Locomotive*, the accident severely scalded two firemen who were on the footplate; one of them died but the driver, who was George Stephenson's older brother, escaped unhurt. Four months later, on 1 July 1828, the boiler of Engine No 1, the famous *Locomotion*, exploded at Aycliffe Lane, which is the present Heighington station, killing the driver. After a rebuild, which *Locomotion* must surely have needed, the engine worked on the railway until 1841.

In 1840 the Railway Inspectorate received its first boiler explosion report from a railway company, which described a 'melancholy accident' that had occurred at Bromsgrove on the Birmingham & Gloucester Railway on 10 November of that year. The only details in the report are that the engine belonged to a Mr Goddard who was hoping to sell it to the B&GR. The directors had allowed it to be given a trial and it was standing on the line after making a few test runs when the boiler blew up, causing the driver's death, and also that of the 'foreman of the engines'. According to *The Rise of the Midland Railway* by E.G. Barnes, the engine was named *Surprise*, and if the godfathers who bestowed this appellative ever intended that it should one day provide a surprise it certainly did so on 10 November. The railway company's report concluded that 'the boiler plate was not strong enough' and the RI's inspecting officers appear to have let the case rest there, not foreseeing that many more such explosions were soon to come their way.

No records of accidents in 1841 are available at the Department of Transport, and the 1842 records do not contain any boiler explosion cases. 1843 was marred by one that happened on the Hartlepool Railway. The company's report to the RI is very brief, the engine not being identified, nor the place, time or what the engine was doing—all that it says is that an old woman, apparently travelling irregularly on the footplate, was killed and that the driver and fireman were slightly scalded. Again, the RI did not take any action.

We come to 1844, by the end of which year 2,236 miles of railway were open in the British Isles, and two explosions are recorded. On 1 May at Carlisle the boiler of the Newcastle & Carlisle Railway engine *Adelaide* blew-up, the enginemen escaping with scalds. The company's report to the RI does not include the time or, what was much more important, what part of the boiler gave way beyond stating that 'the firebox collapsed'. Although the N&C tried to close the incident by declaring that it was due to 'an insufficient supply of water causing a sudden generation of gas' the report also revealed that the engine was 'in the act of starting'. Whether the firebox top was already red-hot, or whether the firebox was on the verge of giving way due to a general state of deterioration, it is evident that the first few blasts up the chimney as soon as the driver had opened the regulator drew up the fire which within a second or two added a few more pounds to the steam pressure that up to then the boiler had managed to contain. The RI apparently accepted the N&CR report and allowed the affair to rest.

When on 11 December a really destructive explosion occurred at about 12.34am on the South Eastern Railway Bricklayers' Arms branch which had been open only seven months the RI's Principal Inspecting Officer, Major General C.W. Pasley, decided to investigate the incident himself, and his report is the first written officially on a locomotive boiler explosion. I have no doubt that Pasley, late of the Royal Engineers, was most knowledgeable where earthworks, bridges and the movements of military traffic were concerned, but it is clear from the report that he had difficulties in fathoming mechanical matters; he described at great length the damage caused by the explosion but appears to have relied on Benjamin Cubitt, the locomotive superintendent of the South Eastern Railway, and also of the London & Croydon Railway, to advise him about the cause.

The train, comprising 11 goods wagons, a second-class 'mail carriage' and a brake van, had drawn away from Bricklayers' Arms station, was crossing a timber viaduct when the engine's firebox collapsed inwards. The explosion hurled the engine, together with the frame and wheels of the tender, over the side of the viaduct, at the same time blowing a great hole through the viaduct's timber deck. The driver was killed and the fireman gravely injured. All that Pasley's report says about the engine, *Forrester*, was that it was new, built by Bury, Curtis & Kennedy of Liverpool and had four wheels; Dendy Marshall's *History of the Southern Railway* rather implies that it was No 78. There is no mention by Pasley of water gauges or safety-valves, which together with their condition should have been fully described, or the working pressure; he wrote rather vaguely that the firebox had 'one side straight and the other circular', which suggests that the boiler was of the Bury design typical of the period, with a semi-circular rear end and no doubt a haystack casing. His summing up was that:

> whether the metal was defective, or not strong enough, or exposed from some cause unknown to an excessive and improper pressure of steam, it certainly failed. Fortunately for the public the explosion of the boiler of a locomotive engine was

very rarely occurred [Pasley did not know what was to come!] but it may be so fatal in its consequences, and is so particularly appalling, that any additional precaution, even though not hitherto customary, is desirable, in order to prevent a similar catastrophe for the future.

The following year, 1845, saw the N&CR in trouble again. The Company's very brief report to the RI said that in the course of working a goods train the boiler of the locomotive *Venus* exploded on 28 January—it omitted the place, time or cause. On the very same day the Manchester & Leeds Railway had an exactly similar experience: the locomotive *Irk* blew-up, causing the deaths of the driver, fireman and another railwayman. It is not quite clear where this happened, for a report from the company to Major General Pasley said 'in the engine shed' and John Marshall's *History of the Lancashire & Yorkshire Railway* says that *Irk*, numbered 27, blew-up in the Miles Platting engine shed. A report of 1857 by Lt-Col Wynne mentions in retrospect that an engine named *Erck* blew-up, calling the incident 'one of the earliest recorded locomotive boiler explosions'. He said that *Erck* 'was projected from a state of rest through the roof of the station shed at Leeds, the steam escaping through a rent in the firebox'. This sounds rather exaggerated; it is quite likely, however, that at least one piece of iron boiler plating penetrated the roof from beneath.

Whether *Irk* and *Erck* were the one and the same is uncertain, but as far as *Irk* is concerned J. Fenton, the M&LR engineer, and W. Fairburn whose firm built the engine, submitted a joint report containing their opinion that the explosion 'arose from the extreme high pressure of the steam having forced the upper part of the copper firebox down upon the furnace'. The accuracy of this description need not be disputed; whether the steam pressure became excessive because the safety-valves had gone wrong or whether the crown sheet was blown-in due to weakness must be left to surmise.

The DTp records for 1846 are incomplete but what papers there are do not mention any boiler explosions. John Marshall's book records the explosion on the L&YR of ex-S&DR locomotive No 18 named *Shildon* or *Shannon*, on 20 November 1846 on the main line a few hundred yards to the north of Sough Tunnel. On 28 June 1847 a goods engine boiler blew-up on the North Union Railway, scalding the fireman, but the type of engine concerned, the place, time and cause remain unknown. On 25 April 1848 a driver and two boys all employed by the North Midland Railway were scalded by 'the bursting of an engine firebox' at Normanton, the time and the cause not having been given. The RI does not appear to have investigated the *Venus* or *Irk* explosions, nor those on the NUR or NMR.

The RI's eyes were turned onto the South Devon Railway in 1849; on 27 June the boiler of the GWR broad gauge engine *Goliah* blew-up. It was one of four 0-6-0 goods engines in the Hercules class, and had gone into service in July 1842. The SDR line to Plymouth had been open only a month when the accident occurred and the company did not have any engines, having put its faith and capital into the atmospheric system which, proving an utter failure, was abandoned in 1848. The GWR supplied engines until 1851 when the SDR engaged a firm to provide locomotive power.

Goliah had started from Plymouth Millbay at 7.30pm in the direction of Exeter, hauling a goods train of eight lightly-loaded wagons and a brake van. Plympton, five miles along the line, was reached without incident; according to the evidence the train passed through the station between 25mph and 35mph, and the driver then 'put on more steam' in order to tackle the two-mile Hemerdon 1 in 42 rising incline that lay before him. Hardly had he done so when there was a violent explosion as the firebox crown sheet gave way under the steam pressure, the engine being thrown off the track and finishing up on its side, facing the way it had come; the fireman was fatally injured but the driver appears to have escaped unhurt.

The RI evidently decided that the time had come for really exhaustive investigations to be made into cases of boiler failure and Capt J.L.A. Simmons was detailed to find out what had gone wrong with *Goliah*. The firebox copper plates were ⅜ in thick. The boiler had two safety-valves, one of the screw balance type set to lift at 70 lb/sq in and another 'adjusted by nuts requiring wrenches to move them'; the latter had been set to open at 150 lb/sq in which 'was double what it ought to have been,' so presumably the boiler's working pressure was 75 lb/sq in. The driver denied having held down the lever of the spring-balance valve in an attempt to increase the pressure for the ascent of the gradient, and Simmons accepted this. It was also averred by the driver that the gauge glass was full when the explosion happened but on this point Simmons disagreed. Although the one fusible plug's metal which was tin, not lead, had not melted he decided that the water level had been allowed to fall and that the crown sheet became bare and was weakened by overheating until it broke away from the copper doorplate. Simmons gathered a considerable amount of evidence but appears to have taken it for granted that the water gauge was working properly, with its portways clear, and that the crown sheet was not carrying scale that might have deprived it of water and caused overheating. Furthermore, the report does not discuss the possibility that cracks started by too-rapid cooling of the firebox when day after day the engine was stabled after working its trains, might have led to the rupture. The RI still had much to learn about the aspects that needed examination after a boiler explosion.

That was the only explosion in 1849, but the following year's records include four. The first was near Darlington on the York, Newcastle & Berwick Railway, a system that an amalgamation of smaller companies had brought into being in 1847 and was later on to become the main line of the NER. On 2 February 1850 0-6-0 goods engine No 35 left Darlington at 4.15pm for Richmond, hauling a goods train of 26 wagons. About two miles along the line and close to the bridge over the River Tees, when, acording to an eye witness, the train was running very slowly, the firebox collapsed, the explosion throwing the engine off the line and breaking it away from its tender. Both the footplate men were killed. The report on the incident, by Capt G. Wynne, is not very convincing. Having consulted two foremen coppersmiths not connected with the railway and taken evidence from them to the effect that the damaged crown sheet displayed all the signs of having been overheated, he concluded that this had happened because the enginemen allowed the boiler's water level to fall below crown sheet level during a two-hour period when they had been shunting at Darlington, and that on starting the journey to Richmond the feed pumps had refilled the boiler until the water that flooded the red hot crown sheet had formed steam in such quantities that the safety-valves could not release it all.

It need not be doubted that the boiler's water level had been too low, and for some time; the real cause of the explosion was almost certainly that during the run from Darlington the crown sheet became so hot and soft that the steam pressure blew it down into the firebox. Wynne did not say in his report whether he examined the boiler's water gauge and whether or not it was in proper order; it could well be that the men mishandled the gauge in some way, or that it was defective and showed a deceivingly high water level as a result. He did however justly comment on the lack of a fusible plug, as No 35 was not fitted with one.

The LNWR found itself in trouble on 26 March when engine No 157 blew-up in a siding at Wolverton. A steam-raiser had kindled its fire at 2.30am and 2½ hours later steam was blowing-off from the spring-balance safety-valves that were set at 60 lb/sq in. When a fitter and mate were detailed to work on another engine standing next to No 157 the mate, finding the noise of escaping steam rather tiresome, screwed down the safety-valve levers as tightly as he could, and the pressure rose to 95 lb/sq in before they lifted again. By 5.55am when the driver arrived, steam was again escaping from the safety-valves, this time 'strongly'. The driver apparently did not notice the pressure being indicated by the spring balances as he oiled the engine and made it ready for work, but 15 minutes later when he opened the regulator the boiler barrel exploded, splitting along the bottom and un-curling until it became an almost flat sheet as it sailed through the air to land 'a considerable distance away'. The only man to become a casualty was the unfortunate fitters's mate; in addition to being badly scalded he had an ear blown-off. Capt R.M. Laffan, who investigated the accident, laid most of the blame on him for tightening the safety-valves, although he also found the boiler's ironwork to be in poor condition.

In June (the date is not known) a four-wheeled engine ten years of age and described as one 'of the old pattern with a circular firebox' came to grief while standing in a siding at Kegworth, a Midland Railway station about 12 miles to the south of Derby. Part of the copper firebox side was blown inwards, which is not surprising as the engine's makers had dispensed with stays that in most locomotive boilers keep the firebox and its casing together, and the ⅝ in copper plates had wasted to only ⅜ in. Of the boiler's two safety-valves, one over the firebox was set so that it released steam at 65 lb/sq in and the other, fitted behind the chimney, needed about 80 lb/sq in to lift it; unfortunately this second valve which because of its heavier loading seldom if ever opened, had become corroded and seized-up. Capt Wynne examined the wrecked boiler and then discovered that the firebox safety-valve's spring was weak and had been releasing the steam at only 56 lb/sq in. He appears to have formed the opinion that the driver, having realised from the engine's performance that the maximum steam pressure was unduly low, had secured the valve in some way in an attempt to get more power from his locomotive but in doing so caused such a rise in pressure that the unduly weak firebox gave way. Wynne's Report does not disclose the number of this early MR engine. No one appears to have been injured.

The fourth explosion of 1850 occurred in the latter part of the year at Staddlethorpe on the line between Hull and Selby, which was by then part of the York & North Midland Railway. The engine, whose number remains unrecorded, had been built by Stephenson & Co in 1839 and was given a new firebox in 1844. It is described as six-wheeled with a tender and was probably, therefore, an 0-6-0 goods, and the boiler had two safety-valves, both set to release at 70 lb/sq in. It was the leading engine of two that were hauling 90 wagons of which 65 were loaded. Capt Wynne, the investigator, has not stated in his report the date or the time when the accident occurred, but he describes how the train left Hull and halted at Staddlethorpe for the drivers to refill their tenders with water. The train was then restarted, but had gone only about ¾-mile along an embankment when the engine's firebox

crown gave way, and the force of the steam as it burst out of
the boiler not only demolished the grate but lifted the engine
off the track, causing it to roll sideways down the embankment slope and come to rest at the bottom, standing on its
wheels. Remarkable to say, both enginemen survived but
sustained severe scalds, and in the fireman's case a broken leg
as well. Wynne's conclusions were that the enginemen had
allowed the water to fall so far below its proper level that the
crown sheet became overheated, and that when the pumps
again covered the hot metal with water such a quantity of
steam was generated almost instantaneously that the safety-
valves, set at 70 lb/sq in, could not cope with it although they
were in good order. He added that 'it is more than probable
that the time had arrived when the firebox should have been
renewed'. The firebox was six years of age and in places $\frac{1}{16}$ in
had wasted from the plates which when new were $\frac{3}{8}$ in
thickness. The report was not one of Capt Wynne's best, his
theory that huge quantities of steam were created almost
instantaneously when cold water flooded a red-hot crown
sheet being ingenious but quite fallacious, although it was not
settled until disproved by practical experiments half a century
later. He may have developed the idea himself but it is more
likely that he had already read of factory boiler explosions
being explained away by similar conjectures. In bygone years,
when far fewer people had any education in science or physics
than is the case today, it was quite commonplace for 'leading
men' to solve mysteries by producing solutions of their own to
satisfy a simple and gullible public—when wireless telegraphy
began, the 'ether' was invented as the mystic medium by
which radio was carried, and so were 'air pockets' to explain
flying accidents in the early days of the aeroplane.

CHAPTER 3

1851 TO 1860

The Explosion Nuisance Becomes a Hazard

1851 passed without the RI becoming aware of any boiler explosions. There was one in 1852 on the Eastern Counties Railway, but all that the records tell us is that on 25 September a fireman was injured on the hand 'in consequence of the firebox roof being blown off, one of the plates being defective'. The place where this occurred, the time and the engine's identity remain unknown, and the RI's officers do not appear to have investigated the incident.

1853 was rather a bad year, with three explosions. The first was on the Midland Railway at Bristol, the engine being of the 0–6–0 tender type, nine years of age and of Bristol & Gloucester Railway origin. The investigation, by Capt. D. Galton, was a little more detailed than those made previously into boiler explosions; his report, which omits the engine's number, was rather wide of the mark in its findings.

The engine left Bristol at 8.10pm with a goods train of 20 wagons for Gloucester. About two miles along the line the train stuck on an incline of 1 in 75 and had been standing about two minutes while the enginemen set about scotching the rearmost wagons, intending to work half the vehicles at a time to the next station, when the boiler burst. The top half of the boiler and the dome were hurled over some lineside cottages, landing nearly 500 yards away, the initial rent having taken place along a horizontal row of rivets; the enginemen escaped injury, being towards the rear of the train. There were two safety-valves set at 65 lb/sq in, one described by Galton as being 'out of the control of the driver' and the other fitted with a ferrule that prevented undue screwing-down. Galton could not, he said, detect any unsoundness in the boiler plates and went to great trouble to prove that the safety-valves were of adequate size. The driver having told him that they were 'blowing off very strongly' at the time of the explosion, he supposed somewhat impulsively that the enginemen had not applied the pumps during the journey from Bristol, although he did not describe the pumps or their condition in his report; he assumed that a deficiency of water had occurred as a result and that 'the top of the firebox became heated and caused a too rapid generation of steam'. How steam could be generated from water that was not there is left unexplained — Galton might at least have taken steps to check that the pumps had been working properly and that the boiler water gauges were in order. In all probability the explosion resulted from defects in the iron barrel that escaped Galton's notice.

At 8.55am on 6 March the Longsight district of Manchester was shaken by a severe explosion when an LNWR engine boiler blew-up in the locomotive shed, which at that time was a roundhouse. Six men were killed, and not only was every window in the building shattered but a sixth part of the roof was blown away and the rest of it lifted bodily a few inches off the walls. The whole of the firebox's outer casing was blown off, the copper firebox was destroyed and the engine's left-hand driving wheel was broken off its 6½in axle.

Capt Wynne carried out an investigation. His report does not give the engine number, nor the type, except that it was six-wheeled, but it was the first report on a boiler explosion in which an inspecting officer was given to really plain speaking. The engine dated from 1840 but by 1846 the company's trains were getting too heavy for it and it was from then on confined to 'pilot' or shunting work. Wynne found some rather startling evidence: during the engine's 13-year life the firebox had never once been renewed and Wynne found that the iron plates forming the firebox casing were 'much honeycombed' by corrosion and eaten away in rings around the stays. The stays themselves were of iron, not copper, and were described by Wynne as 'extraordinary specimens of corrosion, being thickly encrusted in some parts with an oxide, and in other parts greatly reduced in thickness'. He rejected evidence that 25 minutes before the accident a driver was seen screwing-down the safety-valve on the dome, and five minutes later the safety-valve over the firebox, especially as the latter fitting was said to have been 'blown away' and could not be found. When the dome valve was produced, firmly screwed down, he did not hesitate to express his conviction that the shed staff had tightened it 'to save themselves from responsibility which would attach to them for allowing an engine to go out in the condition in which this one was', and he probably had little doubt that the other valve had 'disappeared' to ensure that he did not see it. At the same time he had no intention of attributing the accident to water shortage; in his opinion, previous findings of water deficiencies (including his own!) rested only on conjecture, and he concluded that the Longsight tragedy was due to the neglected state of the engine, which having become a shunting locomotive, had not been getting the same attention as passenger or goods engines.

Capt Galton dealt with the third 1853 case, which occurred at Brighton, on the LB&SCR. Shortly before 7.00am on 17 March 2–2–2 tank engine No 10, dating from 1840, was taken to the passenger station and a locomotive foreman who went with it observed before he left the footplate that the water gauge glass was well filled and that the two safety-valves, one over the firebox and the other on the dome, both fitted with Salter's balances, were set at under 80 lb/sq in. Galton has not told us in his report why this foreman accompanied this engine to the station or what train it was due to work.

A driver with a goods engine nearby said that he saw No 10's driver screwing-down the dome safety-valve and crossed the tracks to speak to him. Noticing that the setting had become over 100 lb/sq in, he told him that 'eighty pounds' was the pressure at which No 10 had been worked previously and was ample; No 10's driver did not respond, however. About five minutes later the dome valve began to blow-off very strongly, he said, and within another minute, at 7.14am, the boiler blew up. The assistant station master and the train guard who were on the adjacent platform saw the driver on the boiler, warming a can of coffee in the escaping steam when the explosion occurred, hurling fragments in all directions and demolishing a good deal of the station roof. Galton's report implies (although it does not confirm) that the driver lost his life but it does not mention the fireman at all.

The boiler was small by modern standards, only 8ft long and of 3ft 4in diameter, containing about 300 gallons of water when in working order. Galton examined the remains of the boiler, which was of the 'long plate' type with four longitudinal seams, and found that 'along the line of fracture' the $5/16$ in iron plating had lost about $1/16$ in of its thickness due to corrosion, which was not unduly serious — an iron boiler of this size with $1/4$in plates ought to have withstood up to 300 lb/sq in internal pressure. He did not see the safety-valves, so presumably they were kept out of his sight; he would have done well to have asked for them and to have tested the Salter's balances, checking their pressure scales against the lever proportions.

Although Galton did not positively attribute the accident to the driver's attempt to raise the steam pressure by screwing-down the safety-valves he implied that this was the main cause, to which the weakened condition of certain iron plates contributed; he recommended that safety-valves should be arranged so that drivers could not interfere with them. A further comment on his part was that the 'long plate' design was 'weak', leaving the reasons for this opinion unsaid. The design was not weak as it happens but with the seams consisting of lap joints, it was very unsatisfactory, for reasons to be explained in Chapter 4. Galton also remarked that boiler plates united by lap joints were liable to bend ever so slightly under steam pressure, doing so on every occasion at the same places and so inducing fractures; this was perfectly true but he did not know why nor did he offer any remedy. The reasons are also given in Chapter 4.

1854 seems to have passed without any boiler explosions but 1855 was a sad year, with five. First of all, the broad gauge 2–2–2 engine *Actaeon* of the Firefly class was in trouble. The makers had delivered it to the GWR in 1841 and it was used for the opening of the B&ER on 1 May 1844. It had 7ft driving wheels and the boiler, with a barrel of $5/16$ in iron plates, had two safety-valves, one loaded to 90 lb/sq in and the other to 88 lb/sq in, both carrying ferrules to prevent tampering. There was a 9in glass tube water gauge, the tube's bottom being level with the firebox top.

When the 6.15am train from Paddington arrived at Swindon on 7 February the engine was taken off and the *Actaeon* was attached, taking the train forward to Gloucester; there *Actaeon* drew off two of the carriages, put one in a siding and was gravitating back towards the train on a down gradient, propelling the other carriage, when the boiler burst. The two safety-valves were blown sky high, falling through the goods shed roof 30 yards away, a piece of the boiler penetrated the wall of a house nearly 300 yards distant, and the bottom half of the boiler was forced down with such violence that it broke the crank axle. Casualties are not mentioned in Captain Wynne's report on the case.

There was no question of excess steam pressure; the safety-valve ferrules were intact and tampering could not have taken place. Wynne found that the boiler's bottom plates had become 'deeply pitted with innumerable indentations, apparently the effect of some corrosive action, and along the junction of the bottom plates with the side plates, on the boiler's right-hand side, there was a deep channel eaten away to some extent, reducing the thickness of the plate to $\frac{1}{10}$ in, evidently the effect of the same action'. 'The conclusion appears irresistible' he went on, 'that the explosion was caused by the plates being so much reduced in thickness as to be no longer capable of resisting the ordinary working pressure of the steam'.

Wynne's report on the *Actaeon* explosion was the first from the RI that mentioned boiler pitting. 'Believing the question [of pitting] to be one of great and growing importance, I applied to Dr Tyndall, Professor of Physics at the Royal Institution', but the only help that this scholarly individual appears to have been able to offer was that 'science probably furnishes the means for its prevention'. Wynne followed this up with a long conclusion, which in brief was that the interiors of boilers needed inspection at reasonably frequent intervals; he revealed that it was almost five years since the interior of *Actaeon*'s boiler had been examined, and therefore since anyone knew what was going on there. His report said that in the majority of explosion cases 'it will be found that the engines have been old and the interiors of their boilers for a long time closed to view'.

Today the causes of the formation of pits in iron or steel boiler plates and tubes are well understood; no easy means of prevention have so far been discovered, a reality that modern amateur operators of steam locomotives would do well to remember. The nuisance is known as differential aeration corrosion and is the result of differences in the amounts of dissolved oxygen in the water that makes contact with the metal surfaces. No iron or steel surface is ever perfect; minute cracks or indentations may be present containing traces of dirt or corrosion products, and these substances restrict the amount of oxygen that gets to the metal surfaces beneath them. Such circumstances set up a very tiny electric cell, the surface having the lesser concentration of oxygen in contact with it, becoming positive or anodic. As the very slight electric current leaves the anodic iron or steel surface it causes the metal to pass into solution and the cell becomes the start of a pit. This microscopic cavity soon becomes covered by a scab or blister of corrosion products which tends to prevent the oxygen-carrying water from getting to the cavity's base, enhancing the electric cell's action and so causing the cavity to deepen. Thus small pits become bigger pits and, just as Jonathan Swift's flea had 'smaller fleas that on him prey and these have smaller fleas to bite 'em', the process proceeds *ad infinitum.*

By 5 April the gremlins that dote on locomotive boilers had arrived at Rugby where LNWR No 164, built in 1847, was shunting wagons in the engine shed yard at 5.50am with a man known as the 'turner' at the controls when the boiler blew-up; the report on the mishap does not say whether there were any casualties, but it quotes evidence given to the coroner, so apparently at least one person was killed. The previous day the engine had been working with the safety-valves screwed-down to 50 lb/sq in; it spent the night in the shed and was taken into the yard shortly before 5.00am. The turner, who seems to have escaped injury, stated afterwards that all the time he had charge of the engine the safety-valves were blowing-off and that the boiler was well filled with water. He did not notice the pressure that the safety-valves were showing and a pressure gauge on the boiler was out of order.

The explosion threw the engine onto its side and completely wrecked it; the whole boiler except for the firebox casing was blown to fragments, a piece that weighed about half-a-ton striking the ground 150 yards away. Wynne could not find any faults with the boiler's material or construction; he was, however, shown the safety-valves which were fully screwed-down. The spring balances that held the valves were not provided with ferrules but the spindles had nuts beneath the levers, which could be readily slackened by anyone who wished to screw-down the wing nuts and so increase the boiler pressure; the range of the screw threads on the balance spindles did not allow the valves to be completely closed but the wing nuts could load them down to 200 lb/sq in. Wynne had little doubt that the wing nuts had, indeed, been screwed-down as far as they would go and concluded that the boiler had burst under this pressure. The person who increased the setting of the safety-valves was never identified, but Wynne criticised the LNWR for letting No 164 leave the shed building and start shunting before it had first been inspected by a 'competent person' who would doubtless have noticed the excessive rating of the valves and the defective state of the pressure gauge.

On the same morning and only half-an-hour after the Rugby explosion there occurred the first recorded explosion of a Scottish engine boiler; Caledonian Railway No 51 blew-up at 6.25am in the running shed at Greenock, killing two men and injuring four others. It was a small engine, the barrel being only 10ft 1½in long and 3ft 6in diameter; the thickness of the iron plates was ⅜ in and the working pressure was given as '80 to 90 lb/sq in'. The fire had been kindled at about 4.30am and only 1½ hours was needed to get up steam. George Wynne, his rank now Lt-Col, found the cause to be almost the same as at Gloucester. A longitudinal lap seam almost at the bottom of the boiler had a deep groove caused by corrosion, about an inch from and above the line of rivets, that had weakened the plate until it suddenly split. The engine was on one of two tracks that entered the engine shed which was dead ended; it was just inside the doorway, and the violence of the explosion lifted it off the rails and overturned it onto the other track, bringing down about half the shed roof as well. Seven years had elapsed since the boiler had last been internally inspected; the locomotive superintendent at the time was Patrick Stirling, who in 1866 took charge of the GNR locomotive department at Doncaster.

On 10 November 1849 the tiny South Yorkshire Railway opened its eight-mile main line from Swinton to Doncaster, extending in the other direction to Barnsley a year or two later. The Midland Railway worked its trains at first, the SYR not having any engines of its own (which is how the LMSR came to have running powers over the LNER to Doncaster that continued until BR was formed in 1948). In due course locomotives were obtained of which 0–6–0 No 8 was bought second-hand early in 1855 after it had worked on the Leeds & Thirsk Railway for an unknown period. At 6.40am on 2 July 1855 No 8 left its shed, presumably that at Mexborough, and a couple of hours later arrived at Aldam Junction, two miles east of Barnsley. It was detached from a train of coal wagons and the driver having climbed down from the footplate told his fireman to take it along the line; the explosion occurred during this movement. Lt-Col Wynne's report does not say that the fireman was killed, but as the explosion overturned the engine and blew the unfortunate man a distance of 80 yards it is unlikely that he survived.

No 8's safety-valves were set at 100 lb/sq in. The driver averred that the gauge glass was half-full of water up to the time of the accident but, the steam having burst the firebox and bent the entire crown sheet flat against the tube plate, Wynne's findings were that water had been deficient in the boiler; he arrived at this conclusion when he found that all traces of scale had gone from the crown sheet's upper surface. The report might have mentioned the condition of the water gauge and of the boiler's feed equipment but did not do so.

From Aldam Junction to Camden Town on the North London Railway, where tank engine No 10 arrived with a train at about 5.10pm on 14 July, 12 days after the SYR incident. The steam dome safety-valve was set at 110 lb/sq in, but so that he could warm a can of tea the driver slackened the firebox safety-valve until it began to lift at about 75 lb/sq in, when he then placed the can amidst the escaping steam. A minute or two later, with the boiler adequately filled with water, the entire barrel was blown apart, leaving the flue tubes exposed to view. The two enginemen apparently escaped uninjured. It was found that one of the iron plates, $\frac{3}{8}$in in thickness, was defective; it had not been properly welded when manufactured and its iron was in layers instead of being solid. Lt-Col Wynne decided that the boiler had given way initially at this weak place and it is certain that he was correct. He should have named the station as Camden Road in his report; the name was changed from Camden Town in 1853, and changed back to 'Town' in 1870.

On 7 April 1856 there was a very violent boiler explosion on the Caledonian Railway main line about three miles north of Carlisle. A seven-carriage mail train bound for Glasgow left Carlisle at 5.56am. It was running at nearly 40mph (and was within six miles of Quintinshill, where Britain's worst railway disaster occurred in 1915) when the locomotive's $\frac{3}{8}$in copper firebox crown sheet split across the middle, the front half being forced flat against the tube plate and the rear half onto the doorplate. Not only was the entire grate blown down onto the track but the locomotive was pulled away from the tender and hurled forward, leaving behind its three pairs of wheels; it turned six complete somersaults before toppling into a field. The tender capsized into the same field and all the carriages became derailed, the explosion having dislodged the track. Both footplate men were killed outright.

Immediately after the accident the CR engaged Professor Rankin of Glasgow to carry out experiments and he set to work to test a similar boiler to destruction, in an attempt to determine what had caused the explosion. Water was forced into the boiler after, it is presumed, the safety-valves had been removed and the openings blanked-off, but when the pressure reached 469 lb/sq in the crown sheet began to give way; the professor thereupon declared that such a boiler's ability to withstand internal pressure was limited to 469 lb/sq in and

Lt-Col Wynne who investigated the incident accepted this profound and learned conclusion.

The design of the firebox roof supports came in for Wynne's criticism, and so it should have done. There were eight longitudinal roof girders, each constructed of a pair of half inch iron strips; these strips were assembled one inch apart and joined by two rows of $\frac{7}{8}$in rivets with, one supposes, suitable ferrules or other distance pieces. The girders were 5in deep except, unfortunately, in the middle where the crown sheet was in most need of support; the two centre girders' depth was reduced to $3\frac{1}{4}$in, to make room for the main steam pipe. Each girder was considerably weakened by its lower line of rivet holes, every hole being slightly less than an inch from the bottom; all the girders broke in half when the crown sheet collapsed.

Experiments were then carried out on two boilers similar to the CR boiler that had blown-up and a lot of figures produced that appear somewhat uninformative, and the findings of Wynne's report were that in addition to the weak roof girders there was, as he had twice said before, 'an evolution of a volume of steam which there are reasonable grounds for supposing may have been generated from the overheating of the firebox, caused by a deficiency of water'. The report did not mention the state of the safety-valves or water gauges, or the last occasion when the boiler was washed-out, and it omits to say whether the boiler had inspection holes that might have enabled shed staff to see whether the interior was clean. In all probability, the roof girders had so much loose scale around them that they and the crown sheet's upper surface were deprived of water, becoming so hot as a result that the crown sheet softened and then gave way, breaking and pulling down the girders with it. In the last paragraph of his report on this CR calamity Wynne said that:

> Since this explosion I have heard of four other similar occurrences but only one of which has been reported to this department, two being unattended with personal injuries to anyone, and the third, though attended with a personal injury which

resulted in the death of either the driver or fireman, having occurred on a private railway, was not reported. It is probable therefore that locomotive boiler explosions are much more frequent than we are at all aware of, and if the still more frequent explosions of stationary engines, attended with such extensive personal injuries, is taken into consideration, with the generally doubtful causes to which they are assigned, the subject assumes an importance requiring a more minute scientific investigation than it has yet received. In saying this I think it due to myself to state that the want of time occasioned by my other occupations prevents my entering on such carefully constituted investigations as I think the subject demands, besides which such investigations would be attended with an expense that I am not authorised to incur.

What Wynne should have said was that it was the duty of the railways' engineers to find the solution, but in 1856 locomotive superintendents were not as yet very experienced; there were virtually no textbooks on boilers that were of any real use, and in drawing offices and workshops there was still much to be learned about boiler design.

The similar occurrence reported to the RI was in Northumberland, where on 11 November a boiler blew-up on the Blyth & Tyne Railway. Opened in 1852 as a tiny coal-carrying line, the B&TR expanded until in 1874, when it was absorbed by the NER, its mileage being 43½. Its main line ran from Blyth to quays at Percy Main where the principal running shed and works were situated, with branches from Backworth to Newcastle and Monkseaton, and from Newsham to Morpeth and Newbiggin. Wynne's report on the incident does not give the place where it happened. The engine involved which was confined to shunting work seems to have been of the Wilberforce type of Hackworth's design, and is described as being 'of a very primitive construction, having been purchased by the Company three years earlier, and having a supposed age of about 20 years'. The boiler was of the 'combined flue and return multi-tubular' type; it contained a longitudinal flue tapered from 2ft 4in diameter at the firegrate end to about 1ft 9in at the back where it entered a 'hot air box'. The heat that passed through the flue into this box then flowed back through 68 1¾ in tubes to a semi-circular smokebox; the fireman worked at the smokebox end of the engine, attending to the fire, and the driver's post was at the other end. We are left to guess for ourselves about the location of the water gauge and whether the driver or the fireman was responsible for replenishing the boiler, the working pressure of which was kept at 60 lb/sq in by two safety-valves. *Derwent*, preserved at Darlington North Road station, is the one remaining example of this type of engine.

The end came when two longitudinal internal stay rods of 1¾ in round iron gave way, allowing the steam pressure to blow the entire front end off the boiler, along with all the tubes and the flue, causing the fireman's death. Wynne's findings would hardly have been accepted today. The engine had been standing 20 minutes, with steam blowing from the safety-valves, while the driver partook of his dinner in a nearby cabin. Wynne said that 'during the 20 minutes the pressure was increasing, owing to the insufficient area of the safety-valves to carry off the surplus steam'. He added that 'the safety-valves of an engine at best will not always keep down the pressure but to meet this there is always a large margin of surplus strength, of which this engine was manifestly deficient, and great blame must attach to the Company for keeping at work an engine in such a dangerous condition'. This observation on safety-valves was dreadful nonsense; it would have been better had Wynne examined and described the B&TR's boiler inspection arrangements and given advice for the future, and had his report stated the thickness of the iron plates and their factor of safety.

The years of 1857 and 1858 ended with a sorry record of ten boiler explosions. Lt-Col Wynne began to investigate his cases more deeply as he came to realise that explosions were most likely due to defects in the boilers unless there was positive evidence of some other cause. Early in 1857 he might have been seen on his way to Lancashire where, at 2.00pm on 19 January, L&YR No 129 blew-up when the doorplate of the firebox's outer casing gave way. The engine was attached to a ballast train that permanent way men were unloading near Sough, to the north of Bolton. Five square feet of iron plate above the uppermost row of the firebox rear stays was torn away from the curved boiler top by the steam pressure, which was only 65 lb/sq in; the piece then broke off at the stay holes and was hurled back across the footplate, where the driver and another man called a conductor who was with him were both killed. The fireman who was underneath the locomotive raking ashes from the grate escaped injury, although the entire train of six wagons and a van passed over him when the force of the explosion drove it forward along the line.

The engine, built in 1839, has not been described by Wynne in his report on the explosion; he did say, however, that the last time the boiler had been retubed and the interior examined was in 1851, 5½ years before the incident. The doorplate was only ⅜ in thick when new, but the piece that blew out had been supported by 13 longitudinal stays of ⅞ in round iron that tied it to the uppermost part of the smokebox tube plate. They were anchored at either end by cotters that secured them in forks which were screwed and riveted into the end plates; these fastenings had become so badly corroded that they had no longer been keeping a firm hold on the doorplate's upper part.

About six weeks later on the MR at Birmingham No 175's boiler blew to bits in the early afternoon of 6 March. The engine, which was confined to yard shunting, had been stabled in a siding and was unattended; the two footplate men had filled the boiler properly before going elsewhere for dinner. The explosion, which apparently occurred with the steam at the maximum working pressure of 85 lb/sq in, shattered the iron boiler, leaving the tubes and firebox completely exposed, and hurling one huge fragment into private premises where it killed a firm's workman. Wynne said that 'the internal surface of the iron plates exhibited that peculiar corrosion of the iron in round pits not unusual in boilers that have been some years in use' — ⅜ in plates that had formed the underside of the barrel had corroded to only $\frac{3}{16}$ in. No wonder the boiler blew-up! Lt-Col Wynne was evidently keeping a good look out for pitting.

Next it was Ireland's turn, the railway concerned being the Belfast & Ballymena opened in 1848, and the first constituent of the LMS(NCC). On 9 April 1857 the locomotive *Eagle* was shunting at Belfast at about 10.00am when the firebox top gave way, killing the fireman who was working the engine's controls on his own; irregularly, the driver was coupling wagons at the time. The downward explosion of steam into the firebox lifted the engine and hurled it about 30 yards, over the top of the wagons that it had been propelling. When Wynne saw that the crown sheet's copper plate was bright and that the lead plug had been fused he at once, and correctly, concluded that the water level had fallen until the crown sheet was bare and became weakened by overheating.

Then on 5 May a driver and fireman lost their lives when at about 11.00am in a siding at Edge Hill a LNWR engine blew-up. Named *St Patrick*, it had been built at Crewe in 1848 and in 1857 by all accounts was confined to shunting. Wynne inspected it and declared that the boiler was worn out. Due to the state of the copper firebox, the entire crown sheet had given way, the copper sides and the corners between the sides and the crown having wasted in places from $\frac{7}{16}$ in to $\frac{1}{16}$ in thickness, until the boiler could no longer withstand the 90 lb/sq in pressure at which it was being worked. A man employed as a boilersmith had noticed the thin areas when nearly a year earlier he had put three patches on the firebox — it seems at the time that he was not unduly perturbed. In 1857, however, boilersmiths still had much to learn; so, it would appear, had the officers and supervisors of the LNWR locomotive department.

Joseph Beattie, locomotive superintendent of the L&SWR from 1850 to 1871, began a six-year series of experiments in 1853 in an attempt to design boilers that would burn coal without also emitting clouds of dirty smoke; up to then the almost universal fuel for railway engines had been coke, which was much more expensive than coal. He was moderately successful, but the problem was finally solved by MR engineers about 1860 when they hit on the idea of the brick arch and firehole air deflector. On 10 October 1857 one of Beattie's 'coal burning engines' met with disaster. Its number is not recorded but it was a 'six-wheeled four-coupled' tender goods engine and had been built only four months earlier. It had two fireboxes, one of more or less orthodox design of copper and placed at the rear of the boiler, and immediately ahead of it the second firebox of iron, cylindrical, and inside the iron boiler barrel. Fairly large flue tubes only a few inches long led from the copper firebox where the fuel was placed to the iron firebox which was called the combustion chamber; ordinary flue tubes connected this chamber to the smokebox. The water space between the boiler barrel and the combustion chamber within it was only 2½ in across. The working pressure at which the safety-valves were set was 120 lb/sq in.

The engine, working the 9.00pm goods train from Southampton, arrived at Basingstoke at 1.05am where a porter asked the driver whether more loaded wagons might conveniently be added. The driver replied that he had hardly been able to get along with the 35 wagons that he already had; he then took the engine to an ashpit and it had been standing there ten minutes when the boiler exploded, both the enginemen being killed.

A locomotive foreman said that he examined the engine some five hours later and found both safety-valves 'tight locked', in other words screwed-down until they could not open at all, but the guard said that the valves had been blowing-off on approaching Basingstoke, so any screwing-down must have been done during the short period on the ashpit. Wynne preferred the guard's evidence, which showed that the valves could not have been screwed-down more than ten minutes at the most, and he said that 'the increased pressure generated in this time could not have been very great'. He added that 'amongst locomotive superintendents I have found an almost universal opinion to prevail that nine tenths of the boiler explosions are caused by the driver tampering with the safety-valves'. The driver with an engine that could hardly haul its train *might* have screwed down the valves to get more pressure, but Wynne was not impressed by the foreman's evidence. Instead, he looked closely at the materials of which the boiler was made. He soon saw that the combustion chamber had collapsed when its iron plating split along a riveted seam; the plate that gave way contained two distinct laminae that had failed to unite properly when the plate was forged. 'It was therefore a weak point' Wynne said, 'from which the effects of corrosion must have sooner or later yielded before the other parts of the boiler were worn out, and therefore the question of whether or not the valves were tampered with is not a matter of such serious importance'. However, Beattie continued to build similar engines, apparently without any further ill luck.

The sixth explosion in the dismal year of 1857 was at Greenwich on the SER, at 8.00pm on 24 November. Wynne's report on the occurrence omits to say whether the two enginemen became casualties, and does not give the engine number, but it tells us that the engine was about to start with an up train when the boiler's entire firebox was blown-in, the force of the steam at 65 lb/sq in lifting the engine off the rails and then dropping it onto the ballast. The copper doorhole plate, originally ⅜ in thickness, had wasted and corroded to only half that amount; Wynne attributed the accident very briefly to 'want of caution on the part of the locomotive department'. J.I. Cudworth was the locomotive super-intendent at the time. However, he continued to hold his post until 1876.

MacDermot's *History of the Great Western Railway* records that the company's broad gauge Firefly Class engine *Leopard* exploded at Bristol in 1857 but the RI's papers do not record the incident.

On 29 January 1858 the boiler gremlins visited the Llanelly Railway, a South Wales mineral system that remained inde-pendent until absorbed by the GWR in 1873, and having up to 1858 a route mileage of 36; the main lines extended from Llanelly Dock to Llandilo and to Brynamman. In the course of ballast train working the 0–6–0 *Victoria* was standing in Pantyffynnon station at about 5.30pm when the boiler blew-up, killing three people and seriously injuring thirteen others. The fireman escaped with slight injuries and the driver was standing well away and was not hurt at all.

Victoria dated from 1841 and was apparently very similar to the B&TR's *Wilberforce*, with the firegrate in an internal 2ft flue tube; it also had a 'hot air' or combustion chamber and 68 1¾ in smoke tubes. The end having the firegrate and smokebox was at the rear of the locomotive; the driver's place, at the other end of the boiler and where the water gauge, three water level test cocks and the steam pressure gauges were fitted, was the leading end. Originally the boiler's working pressure was 80 lb/sq in but it had been reduced to 60 lb/sq in. There were three safety-valves, two of the spring-balance type with ferrules, and the third of a type called a 'stock' valve, but doubtless a 'lock' valve.

The explosion completely shattered the boiler, the steam dome, weighing over 4cwt, landing 150 yards away. Lt Col Yolland, on investigating the incident, found that in many places the plates had corroded from 7/16 in to 5/16 in and in one spot, close to the dome, to only ¼ in. He was satisfied that the feed-water pumps were in good order, his report being the first in which the state of an engine's feed arrangements were mentioned. Having accepted the fireman's evidence that shortly before the accident the safety-valves were blowing-off slightly, and the driver's statement that on approaching the station the uppermost test cock was discharging water, he decided that the explosion 'was occasioned by the ordinary pressure of steam acting against the enfeebled and worn out part of the old portions of the plate on the top of the boiler'. The engine had spent the last seven years of its life on ballast train work, not being powerful enough for mineral traffic; within that period it had been laid up 2½ years, which was probably when most of the corrosion occurred.

Ten days later, on 8 February, the boiler of a LB&SCR engine that was working the 6.00am train from London Bridge to Brighton burst at Caterham Junction (later Purley) station. In the 1850s the portion of the London to Brighton main line lying between Croydon and Purley was shared by the SER and the LB&SCR; Caterham Junction station stood at the divergence of the SER Caterham branch. The engine was nine years old; the boiler's original working pressure was

120 to 130 lb/sq in but this had been reduced to 90 lb/sq in. The explosion occurred when the copper plate at the back of the firebox burst inwards just below the firehole, being forced off the ends of the stays. The fireman was killed, but the engine had been stationary about a minute and the driver may have been away from the footplate for some reason, as it is not recorded that he became a casualty. Lt Col Wynne soon found the cause, which was that the plate, originally ⅞ in thick, had become worn to ¼ in by the coke with which the fire was fed; evidently firemen in those days tumbled the coke into their fireboxes and let it distribute itself about the grate.

The report that Wynne wrote was his last on a boiler explosion and he summed up by saying that 'I desire to take the opportunity of stating that all my experience goes to confirm the view I have for many years taken, that the majority of these explosions occur under the ordinary working pressure of the steam, and can be traced to the boiler being worn out or to some marked defect in its construction, and not to steam of extreme tension generated by the wilfulness of the driver loading the safety-valves, and which is a favourite theory of locomotive superintendents to relieve themselves from blame'.

On 11 June it was once again the L&YR's turn. A poor little 0–4–0 tender goods engine, No 158, built in 1846 and probably similar to *Old Coppernob* in the National Railway Museum at York, was hauling a goods train from Bradford to Holmfirth, having departed from Bradford at 12.55pm — the intended route was through Low Moor, Heckmondwyke, Mirfield and Huddersfield. The train was about a mile beyond Heckmondwyke station when the boiler exploded, the central ring of the three of which the barrel was formed being blown-off and hurled some 70 yards. The fireman was badly scalded and a flying fragment injured a permanent way man, but they were the only casualties. The engine's connecting rods and valve gear received a battering but the train rolled on about 300 yards before coming to rest.

Lt Col Yolland held an enquiry and his report was descriptive and detailed. The boiler, containing 121 brass tubes, was only 11ft 6in long and 3 ft 9 in diameter, with a working pressure that had once been 85 lb/sq in but later reduced to 75 lb/sq in. There were two spring-balance safety-valves, each with a ferrule to prevent undue screwing-down; there was a glass tube water gauge and three water level test cocks, but no pressure gauge. The ring that was blown away had been rolled from a single iron sheet 11 ft 4½ in long, 3 ft 10 in wide and ⁷⁄₁₆ in thick, its ends being united by a lap joint that contained a single row of rivets and lay longitudinally along the bottom of the barrel. Due to severe corrosion the plate gave way along this seam; Yolland found numerous round pits, some an inch across, which had run into one another, reducing the plate's thickness in places to barely more than ⅛ in. In brief, Yolland said, the boiler burst at ordinary pressure owing to its worn-out condition.

The NBR's boiler explosion of 24 July 1858 was the first to occur on that system, of which details reached the RI; Yolland was directed to investigate it, doing so with great thoroughness despite a total lack of evidence on the working of the engine at the time, both footplate men having been killed.

No 66 of the 0–6–0 goods class set out with a mixed train from Edinburgh at 10.15am. At Dunbar the passenger vehicles were detached and the engine continued with the rest of the train, consisting of goods wagons, putting them into a siding at Grantshouse. It then ran light to Reston where eight wagons for Berwick were attached; a stop was made at Burnmouth to attach a ninth wagon and the explosion occurred when shunting it. According to Yolland the engine was 'shattered to pieces' due to the complete collapse of the copper firebox's crown sheet. The boiler was torn from its fastenings and hurled nearly 50 yards by the terrific discharge of steam onto the ground as the grate broke up.

The engine's age was only eight years. Four months before this accident the boiler had been extensively repaired, a new set of flue tubes and 50 new stays having been fitted; a steam pressure gauge was provided, the engine not having had one previously, and there were ferrules on the spring-balance safety-valves to prevent the pressure going beyond 100 lb/sq in. The only defect that Yolland found was a slight reduction in thickness of the firebox's copper sides, but not so much as

to account for the accident; there were no signs of water
shortage or overheating.

An important witness was a telegraph foreman who had
once been an engine driver. He told Lt Col Yolland that
shortly before the explosion he had ridden on No 66 with the
driver who lost his life. The engine, which had a weatherboard
with small holes through which the safety-valve levers extended into the footplate area, was hauling 40 wagons, and the
foreman said that he had noticed that a small wooden wedge
that had been pushed into the weatherboard hole was holding
one of the levers down. He observed that the pressure gauge
was showing 145 lb/sq in and he mentioned this to the driver
who told him that 'the engine could go anywhere with 150
pounds on'. This was not the only occasion when he had seen
this driver, and also another, apply a wedge to a safety-valve
lever.

Yolland accepted this evidence and concluded that the
driver had inserted a wedge in order to get his train more
readily up one of the gradients along the route from
Edinburgh but had then forgotten to remove it, and he
attributed the accident accordingly. Why, if only one valve
was wedged, the other was not preventing the pressure from
rising unduly is not explained very clearly in Yolland's report;
he said 'it would seem as if the safety-valves of this engine did
not work sufficiently freely to prevent an accumulation of high
pressure steam from taking place' but it is much more likely, I
think, that both valves were wedged down. Nevertheless, he
asked the company's locomotive superintendent what was the
designed maximum pressure of the boilers fitted to No 66 and
others of its class, and was somewhat alarmed to learn that this
was not known. He then approached the firm that had built
these engines but their reply was remarkably vague; they said
'the engines had balances supplied to indicate 100 lb pressure
on the valves, and we have no doubt whatever the boilers
would all be tested sufficiently to warrant their being worked
fully up to the pressure indicated with perfect safety'.

In short, the maximum working pressure permitted for No
66's boiler had never been specified and was not known by
anyone. Yolland accordingly recommended in his report 'that

the makers of locomotive engines should, as a general rule, record on a brass plate on the engine the maximum pressure the boiler is constructed to be worked at, and the pressure it has been subjected to in testing it, so that drivers may know the risk they run by tampering with the safety-valves'. It seems so elementary today that every pressure vessel should have its maximum permitted internal pressure marked on it in permanent form that it is difficult to understand why such a need was not appreciated before 1858. However, there has to be a first time for everything.

During his Burnmouth investigations Yolland learned that a similar explosion had occurred at Berwick Station a few months earlier; it was not reported to the RI at the time, and no details are available. It may well be that there were not any casualties and that the NBR kept quiet about the incident.

We pass to 1859, when a blot fell on the SER's copy book. On 16 August the firebox crown sheet in the boiler of No 30 gave way and was forced down onto the tube plate. The accident occurred at Lewisham soon after 10.00pm, but only the fireman was scalded and injured when he was blown from the footplate onto the station platform. Yolland, by this time a colonel, held an enquiry and found that the firebox doorplate had contained a 20 in crack along the seam where the crown sheet joined it and that the initial rupture had begun there. He also revealed that the crown sheet roof girders were too short, resting on the seams at each end instead of on the upright part of both tube plate and doorplate. The crack was on the inner side of the firebox and would have been detected in time by a modern boilersmith carrying an electric lamp; the SER man would have had only an oil lamp or a candle, which is probably why he missed it.

Capt G. Ross investigated the next explosion case, which was on the LB&SCR near Lewes. On the evening of 3 October 1859 goods type 0–6–0 No 108, probably with a tender although Ross has not recorded this, was hauling a heavy goods train up a 1 in 88 gradient near Falmer, on the Lewes to Brighton line, with another engine assisting at the rear, when the firebox top collapsed, just as in the Lewisham accident. The fireman was killed and the driver badly injured. Ross discovered that No 108 also had roof girders that were too short and could not hold up the crown sheet properly but he implied very strongly in his report, though he could not prove it, that the driver had fastened-down the safety-valve levers in order to increase the steam pressure for the ascent of the Falmer incline. When safety-valves fail to open or are prevented from doing so it becomes fortuitous whether the boiler barrel on the firebox is the first to give way.

A fortnight later the boiler of South Yorkshire Railway No 8 blew-up near Wombwell. Only three engines are known to have been involved in such an incident and No 8, the victim of the Aldam Junction explosion of 1855, was one of them. The engine was hauling a coal train towards Mexborough and was about half-a-mile past Wombwell station, with a station master and a guard on the footplate as well as the driver and fireman, when the boiler barrel exploded, throwing all four men onto the ballast; fortunately their injuries were no more than moderate. Pieces of the barrel flew in all directions, the steam dome being flung about 130 yards.

The boiler was another of the type built of longitudinal plates instead of rings. Col Yolland found that the rents in the ½ in plates had taken place mostly along the lines of rivets, but the bottom of the barrel was so badly corroded that the iron was in places reduced to a thickness of ¼ in.

The delightful little Devon town of Totnes is normally quiet but its stillness was violently disturbed on 13 March 1860, when shortly after midday the broad gauge engine *Tornado* exploded in the SDR station, the driver being killed and his fireman badly injured. The firebox's entire outer casing, built of three $\frac{7}{16}$ in iron plates, blew off the boiler, one piece being hurled through the side of the goods shed and another knocking a great hole in the brick wall of a stores building; smaller fragments were thrown up to 300 yards away.

The engine had been built at the Vulcan Foundry in 1854; it was an 0–6–0 saddle tank locomotive, about 38 tons in weight and of GWR design. The casing had the edges of its top sheet riveted over the outer surfaces of the other plates that formed the sides. Capt H.W. Tyler, making his first boiler explosion investigation, found that the inner surface of the top sheet had been eaten away by corrosion just above one of the side plate's upper horizontal edge, until in places there was very little sound metal left. He attributed this mainly to careless applications of a caulking tool with which the riveted seam had been made steamtight when the boiler was built; the tool, he said, had made grooves in the top sheet which corrosion soon enlarged, assisted by the 'working' of the plates when the engine was in motion. He may have been right, but it is more likely that the reasons were those to be described in Chapter 4. Tyler remarked on *Tornado*'s lack of a steam pressure gauge; every railway engine, he said, should have one.

The initial stretch of the Metropolitan Railway (and thus of London Transport), between Bishop's Road, Paddington, and Farringdon, was opened early in 1863. Its construction took three years and almost at the start of the undertaking one of the contractors brought a tender engine called *The Albion* to his work site for shunting wagons of spoil and engineering materials. On 1 November 1860 *The Albion* drew a few wagons out of the Metropolitan Railway tunnel shortly before 8.00am and put them into a siding at the GNR King's Cross station; it was then stationary over an hour. Some shunting followed, then the driver ran the engine up and down a few hundred yards so that the pumps could top-up the boiler. Ten minutes later, while the engine was again stationary, the boiler firebox crown sheet was suddenly torn from the firebox sides and back, and was blown down onto the tube plate. The explosion was so violent that it lifted the engine and over-turned it sideways, bringing death to both enginemen.

Capt Tyler made an investigation, not in the form of an inquiry ordered by the BOT but for the benefit of the coroner who had applied through the Home Office for 'a Government officer' to examine the engine and to give evidence at the inquest. He produced a report for the use of the jury who 'spoke of it in the terms of the highest commendation and expressed a hope that so valuable a document might be rendered available for the public service'.

Tyler was unable to learn very much about *The Albion* except that 'it was admitted to be an old engine' and that the contractor had purchased it from the ECR after, some nine years earlier, it had been given a new firebox in the company's shops. The copper crown sheet was rather light, the plate being ⅜in thick when new and ⅟₃₂ in less at the time of the accident; it was supported from above by six girders each 35¼ in long and at least 1¾ in *shorter* than the firebox, which measured 37 in or slightly more in both length and width, inside. It was because the roof girders were too short that the crown sheet gave way, their ends resting on the riveted seam where the crown sheet was joined to the two end plates, instead of on the end plates themselves, so that far from holding the crown sheet up they tended to press it down. A possible reason for such a bad arrangement may have been that the ECR put second-hand girders from some older engine into the firebox instead of making new ones, selecting the nearest in size that could be found. The boiler does not seem to have had a specified working pressure but Tyler reported that 'it does not appear that this engine was in the habit of working at a higher pressure than between 60 or 70lbs on the square inch'. He wound up by saying:

> boilers should be proved by hydraulic pressure up to twice the strain that they are daily called upon to sustain, not only when first constructed but also periodically in after years. Looking to the frequency of boiler explosions, it becomes a question for serious consideration whether it is not desirable that precautions of this description should be enforced by law. If such precautions were properly enforced, these explosions would be as rare as they are now frequent.

The Engineer of 14 November 1856 recorded on page 582 that a locomotive boiler had blown-up in a Middlesbrough ironworks. The engine had been built by the works staff for internal shunting, its boiler being of curious shape with two steam domes connected by an inverted U-shaped 'saddle'. The boiler split where the saddle had been riveted onto the barrel, killing four men including the unfortunate draughtsman responsible for the design. However, the incident not having been connected in any way with one of the railway companies, the case is not included in the total of 137.

CHAPTER 4

1861 to 1870

Lap Joints and Grooving

During this decade 39 boiler explosions are known to have occurred and grooving was the one cause that predominated. It has already been said that locomotive boiler barrels are normally constructed by joining iron or steel rings that have been fitted telescopically one within the other. The earliest boiler rings were of iron plates that were curved by beating or rolling and then riveted together. At first four plates were needed to form a ring, then as ironmasters developed ways of producing larger plates, three, then two and finally only one. In the early days the horizontal riveted joints were always of the lap type.

It took locomotive engineers a long time to learn that when working pressures well above 100 lb/sq in became normal, lap joints were no longer to be relied upon for horizontal seams, although they were perfectly suitable for the annular seams that connected one ring to the next. Rings containing one or more lap joints were not quite truly circular although the errors would have been considered insignificant and unnoticeable to the eye. Steam pressure, however, tended to distend such boiler barrels into forms that were precisely cylindrical and so caused tiny degrees of bending of the plates, or at least tendencies to bend, that produced localised stress. The lap joints resisted deflection more readily than the rest of the rings and the stresses became concentrated close to and along the lap seams. See Fig 2, page 16.

The amount of this bending or hingeing along the seams varied with the fluctuations that occurred in the steam pressure all the time the locomotive was at work. In due course the hingeing led to minute cracks along the inner side of the barrel; very soon rusting began within the cracks, but the internal inspections that were necessary to detect such corrosion were possible only when all the boiler tubes had first been taken out, which a hundred years ago was not done as often as circumstances demanded. After a while the cracks became grooves or furrows which eventually weakened the rings so gravely that if the plates were not renewed in time the boiler split and burst open.

Grooving could usually be discovered in time if boilers were examined internally at intervals no longer than three years, but unfortunately tubes need to be cut at the firebox end to enable them to be taken out of a boiler and cannot be put back, and new tubes have to be fitted in their place. Internal inspections are thus large and costly operations and railway managers tended to postpone them, particularly at times when they were having difficulties with their balance sheets. The introduction of double-strip butt joints for longitudinal seams solved the grooving problem, but locomotive boiler builders were decidedly slow to adopt them. Indeed, grooving continued to cause explosions until 1890 (the explosion at Seaton, 27 November) but had locomotive engineers paid better attention to a paper read before the Institution of Mechanical Engineers in 1866 by William Kirtley, who became the locomotive superintendent of the London, Chatham & Dover Railway in 1874, they might have adopted butt joints much sooner than they did, and many explosions would then have been avoided. The paper revealed all the evils of lap joints, as did a report issued by the MSUA in January 1869.

Of the 39 cases, 20 were investigated by the Railway Inspectorate, the first having occurred at Mill Street station, Newport, on the Monmouthshire Railway on 1 April 1861. This railway has been described by MacDermot in his *History of the GWR* and was very old; starting as a tramroad in about 1800, conversions to a standard gauge system began in 1852 and it was amalgamated with the GWR in 1880, its mileage by then being 51.

At 8.05am engine No 1 was standing 'at the end of the platform', heading an empty wagon train, when the boiler barrel burst, injuring two firemen left on the footplate by the driver while he went away to consult the guard. No 1 was of the 0–6–0 tender goods class, with 18 in cylinders, 24 in stroke, 5 ft wheels and a working pressure of 120 lb/sq in, giving a theoretical tractive effort of 15,552 lb; it was a powerful engine for the period in which it was built. The boiler, 12 ft long and 4 ft 3 in across, was of ⅜ in iron and the barrel had three telescoped rings, each containing two horizontal lap joints that lay more or less along the barrel sides. The company had possessed the engine about 6½ years, during which time it had run nearly 90,000 miles without having been re-tubed and therefore without any internal inspection of the boiler. Col Yolland on investigating the incident found that during this period cracks had developed along the tops of the lap joints, in places half-way through the iron. He was satisfied that the boiler had split along these cracks but he did not entirely manage to discover the cause — his report says:

> it is quite possible that marks made by caulking tool may have had something to do with the origin of these cracks but they are probably mainly the result of the greater rigidity of the plates at this part when opposed to the greater flexibility of the adjacent part of the boiler plates.

Capt Tyler investigated the next explosion, which occurred close to a fairly high bridge over the line, called the Easenhall Bridge and about four miles north of Rugby on the LNWR. On 4 July 1861 at about 10.40pm Bloomer class 2–2–2 No 249 was hauling the 8.25pm Irish Mail from Euston on its way to Holyhead when the boiler barrel blew into seven or eight pieces, many of them striking the bridge piers in their flight. The engine's right-hand 7 ft driving wheel was broken off its axle by the impact of one of the pieces and also collided with a bridge pier; the engine itself, which was almost destroyed, fell over as it came to rest, derailing all eight passenger train vehicles behind it. The driver, who was hurled off the footplate by the explosion, fell against a telegraph pole and sustained some injuries but the fireman was killed; the guard and a post office clerk were slightly injured but the passengers all escaped with 'alarm and severe shocks'.

The Bloomers were built for speed rather than power, and No 249's tractive effort was only 8,000 lbs. The boiler was tiny by modern standards, being only 11¾ ft long and 4 ft in diameter — the whole engine less its tender weighed only 29 tons. The results of the explosion show all too clearly what may happen to even a small boiler when as in this case the barrel gave way under steam pressure of no more than 120 lb/sq in. Once steam pressure is raised in any boiler the iron or steel plates become stretched and then the slightest rent that develops is extended in all directions by the tension until the barrel bursts into pieces, just as a toy rubber balloon stretched by being inflated splits open instantaneously when a pinpoint causes a minute rupture.

The cause was the same as in the Newport case — grooving in the barrel's ⅜ in iron plates, along the lap seams, had reduced the thickness in places to only ¹⁄₁₆ in. Tyler believed that the damage had occurred during the last 10 years that had elapsed after the delivery of the engine to the LNWR in 1851 and that the start of the grooving had not been noticed when re-tubing took place in 1857. 'The only method', he said, 'by which accidents of this description can be properly provided against is by more frequent examination'.

The scene moves to Stella Gill, Co Durham, on the NER. On 23 September 1861 at 9.00pm an 0–6–0 goods No 84 was about to start with a coal train when the boiler barrel burst, badly injuring both footplate men and killing the guard who was sitting on the engine buffer beam. The barrel, 10 ft long and 3½ ft across, was another of the 'long plate' type, built of four 10 ft plates joined by four longitudinal lap seams running the barrel's full length, two of them below the water level. Grooving had developed along the left-hand lower seam until in places only ¹⁄₁₆ in of iron plate was left, and eventually the barrel split open. Capt Tyler after investigating said that 'more frequent inspections and examinations should be made than at present' but he also criticised the manner in which the boiler's firebox end had been fixed firmly to the engine frame by 'hanging brackets'. He recommended 'the more recent method, introduced by Sharp, Stewart & Co, of securing the boiler to the framing at one end by means of sliding angle iron junctions, so as to allow the boiler to expand and contract without strain between it and the framing'.

What exactly happened when an engine boiler burst on a colliery line at Cramlington, Northumberland, on 20 February 1862 remains unknown. The incident was put on record only by the MSUA and apart from stating that the explosion 'injured three persons', no details were given.

The LNWR main line was in the news again on 5 May 1862. 0–6–0 goods engine No 878 was about to start away from Harrow with a 24-wagon train when the right-hand side of the barrel split open with a violent explosion. Both enginemen were struck by boiler tubes which were torn away from the front and wrenched back over the roofless footplate, the fireman being killed. Delivered new by the makers in 1853, the boiler had been re-tubed in October 1860 but Capt Tyler would not accept that severe grooving along one of the middle ring's lap joints, which was the cause of the explosion, had developed all within the 20 months or so since the tubes were replaced. Either there were already signs of grooving in 1860 that were observed by someone who decided, very wrongly, to let the plates give further service or else the barrel had not been inspected properly. 'This and other instances', he wrote, 'prove sufficiently that additional care and attention are much required in the maintenance of the steam boilers of locomotive engines. The common practice that exists of allowing boilers to run six or seven years without internal examination is evidently a most dangerous one'.

Attention was next turned towards Paddington, GWR, where on 8 November 1862 broad gauge 4–2–2 *Perseus* was standing in steam within the engine shed. At 5.45am there was a frightful explosion as the boiler barrel disintegrated, *Perseus* being thrown ten yards and wrecked — the lighter-up who had raised steam in the engine boiler and two engine cleaners all lost their lives.

Grooving adjacent to a lap joint along the bottom of the boiler's middle ring had weakened the $7/16$ in iron plate until the prescribed working pressure could no longer be contained. Capt Tyler inspected the ruined boiler and repeated in his report that 'additional care and attention are much required in the maintenance of boilers', adding that 'it is most unsafe to allow an engine to run on without any examination of the interior of the boiler, as the *Perseus* has done, at full pressure, for 7 years and 5 months, and for a duty of 175,000 miles'. Hardly a compliment to Daniel Gooch who was still in 1862 locomotive superintendent of the GWR!

The bursting of a boiler barrel on the NER at Arthington, about nine miles to the north of Leeds, on 20 October 1863 was recorded by the MSUA but the RI's papers do not appear to mention the case. The only details noted by the MSUA were that the barrel gave way due to internal grooving, one 'person' being killed and two others injured.

During the morning's early hours on 5 May 1864 goods 0–6–0 No 356, built in 1854, was ready to leave Colne on the Midland Railway when the boiler barrel burst, 16 large pieces of jagged plate and many smaller bits flying in all directions. The roof of a house nearly 500 yards away was penetrated by the safety-valve fitting, which injured an old woman as she lay in bed. The extensive damage to the engine prompted the *Preston Guardian* to report that 'a more complete wreck was never witnessed'.

Capt Tyler issued a pretty scathing report on the incident, which may have influenced William Kirtley to compile the paper of 1866 already mentioned. Having revealed that corrosion along the top of a lap joint in the foremost of the boiler's three rings, below the water line, had nearly eaten through the $7/16$ in iron plate he decided that the explosion had started there. He referred to six previous similar cases and wrote:

> these seven cases represent a more serious amount of risk than would appear at first sight, that is daily incurred by the officers and servants of railway companies as well as by the public. Of the 6,500 locomotive engines and upwards which are in use on the railways of the United Kingdom, a large proportion are affected by corrosion to an extent which is more or less dangerous. For every engine that explodes there are a great number of others

which have been much weakened from this cause, and which are constantly working with a less margin of safety than ought always to be preserved between ordinary pressure and bursting pressure.

Then he advised that:

boiler barrels should be made more perfectly cylindrical by the use of butt joints and cover strips in place of the lap joints more commonly used. The longitudinal joints should be placed in all cases above the water line instead of below it, so as to prevent the risk of corrosion, and the boiler should be firmly attached to the framing at one end only, the other end being allowed to slide backwards and forwards, to allow for expansion and contraction.

To what extent these comments influenced Matthew Kirtley (who was William Kirtley's uncle and the locomotive superintendent of the MR from 1844 to 1853) remains unknown, but only one further case of a boiler explosion on the 'Midland' has been recorded.

When the Metropolitan Railway opened in January 1863 between Bishop's Road (on the present Hammersmith & City line and re-named Paddington in 1933) and Farringdon the line was of mixed gauge. The GWR worked it with broad gauge trains until August 1863 when the GNR took-over the operation, using standard gauge engines and carriages. In due course the Metropolitan Railway obtained rolling stock and worked the services itself. On 9 May, only four days after the Colne explosion, the GNR engines that were hauling Metropolitan trains included No 138, one of the 31 tender 0–6–0s that were the GNR's first goods engines, built in 1850 and 1851. At 9.05am No 138 was about to leave Bishop's Road with a passenger train for Farringdon when there was an almighty blast as the boiler exploded. The two enginemen, a 'breaksman' who was standing on the adjacent platform, and a passenger in another train that was entering the station were all badly injured, and a cabman standing over 100 yards away had a narrow escape when a heavy falling fragment of the barrel cut a piece out of his hat. There was a fair amount of damage to the station.

Capt Tyler soon found that the barrel had given way where the left-hand side of the boiler's middle ring had been heavily grooved by corrosion along a lap joint, leaving only $\frac{1}{16}$ in of iron in parts. He repeated the advice he gave in his Colne report and had the recommendations been followed promptly by the locomotive engineers many of the later explosions would not have happened. Nevertheless, there was another aspect. When railways began, the engineers can have had little idea of what locomotive maintenance was going to cost. It is very likely that by the 1860s corrosion damage to boilers and the rate at which it occurred was taking locomotive super-intendents by surprise, all the more so as working pressures were increasing. The company directors' budgets allowed so much for locomotive running and no more, and there can be little doubt that on many if not most railways, managers were having to work engines up to and beyond the borderlines of safety, in the same way that captains were being intimidated into setting out with vessels that were unseaworthy and, until the Plimsoll Line was imposed in 1876, often heavily overladen.

From Bishop's Road, Capt Tyler was soon on his way to Overton, a station on the LNWR three miles west of Peterborough and later to be re-named Orton Waterville. On 30 May 2–2–2 tender locomotive No 897 had just drawn the 11.55am passenger train from Peterborough into the station and about 40 people were preparing to get out of the five carriages when the boiler barrel ring adjacent to the firebox blew completely off and landed 50 yards away. The explosion broke the engine's crank axle and seriously damaged other parts but both enginemen escaped with moderate injuries.

Built in 1849, the engine had originally belonged to the South Staffordshire Railway, bearing the number and name 297 *Dudley*; it passed into LNWR hands when the SSR was leased to the company in 1861. Grooving along a lap seam had led to the explosion. Tyler said that 'the engine was 15 years old and its boiler much patched but its interior had, never-theless, not been examined for nearly 4½ years'. He again repeated the recommendations made in his Colne report.

The North London Railway, opened in 1850 from the LNWR goods depot at Camden Road, was originally intended as a route for LNWR goods trains to and from the London Docks at Poplar. A connection with the London & Blackwall Railway enabled the NLR to work passenger trains from Camden Road to Fenchurch Street, and this service to and from the City proved so attractive that the company was soon running the trains at 15-minute intervals, continuing to use Fenchurch Street until Broad Street was opened in 1865. The LNWR provided motive power until 1853 when the NLR began its own locomotive department with a fleet of ten 2–4–0 tank engines, opening a locomotive works at Bow. In 1851 the line was extended from Camden Road to Hampstead Road (re-named Chalk Farm in 1862 and now Primrose Hill), joining the LNWR there; this enabled NLR passenger trains to reach Kew Bridge and Richmond.

16 August 1864 was a bad day for the NLR. The 9.32am train of five carriages from Chalk Farm to Fenchurch Street, hauled by No 4, arrived at Camden Road at 9.34am, where it was scheduled to await the arrival of the 9.05am train from Kew to Fenchurch Street — the engine came to rest on the bridge over Randolph Street. When the second train of six carriages arrived at 9.39am the engine was detached and run to the other end; it then closed the six carriages up to the five ahead to make an 11 carriage train which No 4, chimney leading, was to take forward. The two portions were coupled and the guard was looking for the stationmaster's handsignal for the train to be started when there was a terrifying explosion in the engine firebox. Both enginemen were flung off the footplate, the driver tumbling onto the platform, badly injured, and the fireman losing his life when he fell headlong into the six-foot space between the tracks.

No 4 was a 2–4–0 tank engine built in 1854; the pressure in the boiler while stationary at Camden Road was 120 lb/sq in and the water gauge glass was well filled. The explosion occurred when the whole of the copper firebox's left-hand side was blown into the firebox, and as soon as the great clouds of steam had drifted clear of the station the somewhat startled

North London Railway engine No 4 at Camden Road after the explosion of 16 August 1864. (*Illustrated London News*)

people in the carriages would have been additionally astonished to observe that the locomotive which had been at the head of their train had now vanished. The explosion's effect was to tilt the engine to the left, against the bridge's masonry parapet; the parapet gave way and the engine then dropped into Randolph Street 20 ft below, landing on its wheels after twisting round in its fall, end for end. The *Manchester Courier* reported that 'the alarm of the passengers, who rushed frantically from the carriages, may be better imagined than described. They were seen running in every direction and great confusion prevailed'. However, none of these people was injured by the incident. The *Courier* went on to say that the explosion 'somewhat shattered the wooden girders supporting the bridge'; the NLR engineers must have decided pretty quickly that both the bridge and its tracks were still quite safe, as the train service was resumed in little over an hour.

Capt Tyler examined the wrecked firebox closely and saw that the torn copper side, which measured 3 ft 6 in by 4 ft 8 in, had been held to the outer shell by 108 ¾ in copper stays. The side had been forced off 89 of these stays, from which the heads and ends had been burned away almost completely by the fire; the other 19 stays were all broken, many of them having already been fractured through before the disaster occurred. All 108 stays had been in position throughout the ten years that No 4 had been at work. Tyler's report says that: 'the engine has been working for some time in a critical condition'. It certainly had, but Tyler might have pointed out as a lesson to other railways that the NLR running shed arrangements for periodical boiler inspections seem to have been somewhat relaxed to say the least, and that the space around the firebox, at 2¾ in, was far too narrow to contain sufficient water for the protection of the copper plate and the stay heads from overheating.

Internal grooving along a lap joint ended the life of a Blyth & Tyne Railway engine on 29 August when the boiler barrel burst at Percy Main, probably at the locomotive depot; the MSUA record says that there were two casualties, one fatal. The RI does not appear to have heard of the case, possibly because on the B&TR as well as on many other railways there was in the nineteenth century an impression that accidents in the works were not reportable to the RI, and in those days a railway's principal running shed was often amongst the works repair and construction shops.

The year 1864 closed with an explosion on a colliery line two miles from Barnsley on 24 December; the MSUA recorded the incident but without any details except that there was one fatality.

No details have been passed down of an explosion on the L&YR when the year 1865 had scarcely begun; the MSUA said briefly that it occurred on 6 January at Hightown, presumably the station of that name on the Liverpool to Southport line.

In December 1864 GNR 2–2–2 No 98 had its wheels taken out in a workshop adjacent to the running shed at Peterborough and was placed on two trollies. While the wheels were under repair the boilersmiths took the opportunity to work in the firebox. On Saturday 14 January 1865 the boiler was filled, and a foreman ordered steam to be raised so that seams and joints could be tested for leaks. By 5.00pm when steam pressure was 125 lb/sq in there was a thunderous explosion, all the worse because it was in a building; the two foremost rings of the barrel's three split open along a grooved lap seam. Three repair shop workers were killed, a fitter badly injured and the workshop and its roof blown almost to pieces, as well as the engine being wrecked and several others damaged.

Capt Tyler said in his report that 'it was an act of the highest imprudence thus to bring in an engine, 13 years old, and to test it for leakage under 130 lb/sq in of steam pressure (the pressure that the foreman had required). And it was a totally unnecessary risk because the boiler might have been tested more quickly, quite as cheaply and more effectively by water pressure, without the slightest danger'.

Wise observations, but hydraulic testing in a running shed's repair shop is not always easy. The RI had first advised boiler pressure testing with water some five years earlier and frequently repeated this counsel, but it is unlikely that they realised what it involved. Whereas when a boiler is in steam the fire maintains the pressure despite small steam leakages here and there through valves and pipe joints, water is virtually incompressible and the slightest leak will render an hydraulic pressure difficult if not impossible to create. To test a boiler, therefore, the safety-valve assembly must first be removed from its opening in the boiler which must then be blanked by an iron plate and a gasket joint that will be absolutely pressure-tight. Then the regulator valve must be dealt with similarly, by opening and afterwards re-closing the steam dome. All other openings provided for steam valves, water gauges and injector clacks must also be covered, all these tasks consuming much fitters' time; care is necessary to ensure that the water fills the boiler completely, without trapping any air, and only then can a satisfactory hydraulic test be effected.

A month later, on 12 February 1865, Leominster station on

the GW&LNW Joint Railway was shaken by a severe boiler explosion at about 2.30am. This time it was not grooving that was responsible, but corrosion of a different sort. GWR No 108 was working a goods train from Hereford to Birkenhead, and after shunting at Leominster was about to proceed with it when the boiler barrel burst. Capt Tyler's report does not mention casualties but the station buildings, occupied at the time by the stationmaster and his family, were greatly damaged.

No 108 had started life in 1849 as 0–6–0 tender goods engine No 11 of the Birkenhead Railway, passing in 1860 to the GWR which re-numbered and rebuilt it in 2–4–0 tender form. The boiler, constructed in 1860, had two rings, each 5 ft long and of equal diameter, that were butted together and joined by a 7 in iron belt riveted around them on the outside. Instead of being in close contact the rings were 1¼ in apart, the belt covering the gap; the belt became weakened by internal corrosion within the gap until steam pressure burst it apart and tore the front ring to pieces.

Many people know the village of Coxhoe in Co Durham only as the birthplace of Elizabeth Browning, but in 1865 it became familiar to the NER directors for a different reason; on 20 March their engine No 122 blew-up there. It was hauling 22 empty ballast wagons from Ferryhill to Hartlepool, and running tender first had just re-started after a halt when the entire boiler barrel split open, causing the driver's death.

The engine, built in 1851, was an 0–6–0 goods and somewhat small, with 14½ in cylinders and a boiler barrel 10 ft long and only 3½ ft in diameter. The boiler, working at only 90 lb/sq in, was another of the long plate type, similar to that which exploded at Stella Gill, but having five longitudinal plates and five seams; the barrel was uncurled by the explosion and it fell, flattened-out, 220 yards away, in a field. The engine was more-or-less destroyed. By the time Capt Tyler received instructions to look into the case the wrecked boiler had been disposed of and he could not examine it, but he was told that a seam had given way not due to grooving but through a line of rivet holes, which he appears to have accepted.

It is much more likely that grooving or some other similar internal defect was the real cause and in all probability Edward Fletcher, locomotive superintendent of the NER from 1854 to 1882, got rid of the wrecked boiler to ensure that Tyler did not get a chance of seeing for himself where the faults lay. Tyler's report contains a good deal of rather vague supposition 'the iron of which the barrel was composed', he said 'was evidently common Staffordshire plate, unfit for such a purpose', and 'there must apparently have been defective workmanship, to which boiler work as ordinarily performed is always more or less liable, in addition to the employment of an inferior quality of iron and to an objectionable system of construction in order to produce explosion'.

The boiler plates were of ⅜ in iron and the seams had ¾ in rivets at 1¾ in pitch; at 90 lb/sq in the tension on the seams was therefore under 9,000 lb/sq in and the plates would not have broken through the line of rivet holes unless the iron had been in a very bad way indeed. So if grooving were not the answer there was only one other solution — the safety-valves had been held down by some means or other.

It may be because no one was actually killed when the boiler of a GWR narrow gauge engine exploded at Chester on 30 March 1865 that the RI did not investigate the case. A small note in the BOT records says that the incident occurred at the station and that the driver and fireman, a guard, 'breaksman', switchman, watchman, shunter, numbertaker and 'a stranger' were all injured. The MSUA seems to have collected some information, however, the Association's records saying that there was one fatality (one of those injured may have died some time after the RI decided not to act) and that grooving was the cause of the explosion.

Only the MSUA records mention an explosion of a week later, on the GNR at Wakefield. On 7 April 'one person' was killed when an engine's boiler barrel burst due to a longitudinal seam giving way. A week after that, on 14 April, the boiler of an Edinburgh & Glasgow Railway goods engine blew up at Stirling, a parcels clerk being killed and the driver injured. That is all the RI recorded, but the MSUA has given the cause as 'internal corrosion'. The RI papers contain a brief note saying that a passenger train's engine boiler burst at Miles Platting station on the L&YR on 26 May 1865, a piece of boiler plate killing an unfortunate boy who was in a field alongside the line. There does not seem to have been an Inspecting Officer's Inquiry, probably because the RI was told that passengers and railway staff escaped injury; according to the MSUA, however, 'a person' was injured as well as the boy's death, and grooving caused the explosion. All that can be learned about an exlosion on the NER at Bishop Auckland on 6 June is from a MSUA note saying that four people were injured; the RI does not appear to have been told about it.

Capt Tyler must have formed a poor impression of affairs on the Blyth & Tyne Railway when he visited it at the end of 1865 after a 2–4–0 tender passenger engine belonging to the Company had blown-up shortly before 8.00am at New Bridge station, Newcastle, on 15 December, when its enginemen were killed. After a spell of shunting the engine, No 25 and built in 1862, had been stationary a minute or so when the whole of the copper firebox's left-hand side gave way under steam at 120 lb/sq in; the engine was torn from the tender by the explosion, spun completely round and overturned. Tyler found that the firebox was in a most neglected state; copper stay heads that should have held the left-hand side were mostly burned away and the plate itself wasted by fire action, the boiler bursting when the stays lost what little hold they had left.

The organisation at the B&TR's works at Percy Main seems to have been pretty rough; Tyler's concluding remarks in his report were:

> that some additional records are required at the Percy Main works, inasmuch as there were no means of knowing, except from the memory of the foreman boilersmith, and from actual observation of the firebox, either the period or the extent of the repairs which had been done to it about a month before the explosion; and these two means did not afford precisely the same result.

The fact is that after the steam locomotive had been initiated on the railways of Northumberland and Co Durham, railway development on the Tyneside stood still and was soon being outstripped by the designers and creative workers of Crewe, Derby and Swindon. The men who worked railways such as the B&T were content to plod along in the steps of their ancestors, leaving the advancement of works and running shed organisation, together with the invention of the injector, the brick arch for the firebox and the Ramsbottom safety-valve, to others. It was not until 1898 that W.M. Smith of Gateshead brought railway prestige back to the Tyneside by producing the famous Smith compound system that proved so successful on the NER, the MR and then on the LMSR.

The only records of explosions that occurred during 1866 and 1867 are those left by the MSUA; the RI does not appear to have heard of the eight incidents occurring in those years. On 1 January 1866 a boiler 'gave way' on the GNR at Nottingham, apparently without causing casualties as none are mentioned; longitudinal grooving was blamed. An exactly similar accident happened on 14 February at a place on the NBR, described by the MSUA as 'Dunse' but which may have been Duns on the branch from Reston to St Boswells — 'one person' was injured. Internal grooving is also given as the cause of an explosion at Nottingham on the MR, when on 19 June three people were injured. The explosion that occurred at Sunderland on a colliery line on 7 August was more serious; one man was killed and three others injured when a firebox's lefthand side was blown off its stays, the copper plate having been wasted by fire action until it was only ⅛ in thick. Then on 10 August tragedy struck the NBR at its station in Edinburgh when a mudhole door blew-out and 'a person' was killed, either being struck by the door itself or by the deluge of escaping steam and water.

The first of three 1867 explosions was at Shildon on the NER; one man was killed and another injured on 10 May when a boiler barrel burst, due to grooving. One man became a casualty but luckily escaped with his life on 24 July at Bilton Junction, Alnmouth, also on the NER — the left-hand side of an iron firebox casing blew off its stays. The third case, of which no details at all have been recorded, was on 2 September at Plashetts on the NBR line that lay through the North Tyne valley between Reedsmouth and Riccarton Junction.

The year 1868 started with an explosion at Halshaw Moor, L&YR, on 31 January. No 115 of the 2–2–2 tender class was working the 5.30pm passenger train from Manchester to Bolton and had just made a scheduled stop when the left-hand side of the firebox was blown-in. The driver was very seriously injured but the fireman was down on the track, about to sand the rails so that the train would re-start easily, and he managed to avoid the huge discharge of steam. Col Yolland, making an investigation, found that the copper plate, originally ½ in thick, had been burned away until in places the thickness was *less* than ⅛ in; it had split down the middle and the two halves then ripped off the stays and folded back, one against the tube plate and the other over the firehole. The copper stays had been holding the plate in position until their heads were so burned away that they could no longer retain it.

None of the L&YR principal locomotive officers appears to have advanced any explanations to Col Yolland for the condition of the firebox. In his report he wrote that 'it is apparent that the engine must have been running for some considerable time with an insufficient margin as regards the strength of the firebox'. The Inquiry revealed that the firebox had been in service 16 years and that during that time the engine had run 451,000 miles.

The only other explosion known to have occurred in 1868 was on 14 July at Sowerby Bridge, L&YR, the incident being recorded only by the MSUA; three men were injured but no one killed, it seems, and grooving was the cause.

The RI does not appear to have investigated either of the two explosions that happened in 1869 but in neither case were any lives lost. One is inclined to suspect that at this time the BOT was judging the seriousness of a boiler explosion by the gravity of the casualty list, which was not a very good policy, the whole principle of the RI investigation procedure being to find out what went wrong and to recommend remedies.

The first explosion was at Middleton, on the L&YR and at

the end of a short branch from the line between Manchester and Todmorden. The only record of the case is amongst the MSUA's papers and says that on 22 January a boiler 'gave way in the barrel' due to internal grooving. There is no mention of casualties so very likely everyone who was around the engine escaped injury. The RI papers, however, contain a brief note of the second case which was at Stonehaven on the CR: on 9 December the boiler of 'a pilot engine of a goods train burst'. The train concerned was evidently double-headed as the driver and fireman of the pilot engine and the driver of the train engine were injured. The MSUA added in its brief record that the pilot engine belonged to the Scottish North-Eastern Railway.

The first nine months of the year 1870 appear to have passed without any engines blowing-up, but the MSUA recorded that on 1 October a man was killed on a colliery line at Dowlais when a boiler 'gave way in the firebox'. As the copper plates were afterwards found to have been wasted until in places their thickness was only $\frac{1}{32}$ in it is surprising that the firebox held out as long as it did. The RI papers do not mention the case.

There is no longer a station at Deepcar on the main line of the late MS&LR. It lay in the delightful wooded Don Valley and was normally very quiet, but far from quiet on 25 October 1870 when No 83, working the 4.45pm passenger train from Sheffield to Penistone, was re-starting after passengers had been set down. Three iron plates forming the top and sides of the boiler at the firebox end blew into the air, one of them landing near the River Don, 500 yards away; the explosion killed the driver and threw the fireman onto the adjacent platform, fortunately without injury.

No 83, a 2–4–0 built by Hawthorns of Newcastle in 1849, was an unlucky engine — only eight days earlier it had come to grief within a mile or two of Deepcar when one of the coupling rods broke. Lt-Col F.H. Rich, making his first burst boiler investigation, attempted to seek the cause, but by the time he came to examine the shattered plates they were so rusty that he could not detect any faults; however, Charles Sacré, the locomotive superintendent, showed him a place along one of the fractures and declared it to be a flaw left in the iron at the time of manufacture, Rich accepting this and attributing the explosion to its presence.

Sacré told Rich that the boiler had received an hydraulic test in 1863 to 200 lb/sq in and in 1870 to 130 lb/sq in, but Rich declared in his report 'that a cold water test is not satisfactory for proving steam engines; I would suggest that they should be pressed with steam to double the working pressure. This might be effected, without danger to the lives of the persons employed in proving them, by placing the locomotive under test, between two large earthen or masonry traverses'. Rather a ruthless way of routine testing! However, it is unlikely ever to have been adopted.

One man was injured at Woodford on the GER, according to the MSUA, when an engine boiler exploded on 3 November but there are no more details to be had.

The number and class of the 2–4–0 outside-cylinder tender engine that blew up at Northallerton, NER, on 29 December 1870 were not included by Lt Col Hutchinson when he wrote his report on the incident. The engine, built by R. Stephenson & Co, was delivered to the NER early in 1847 and its boiler, of the lap-jointed long plate type having six iron plates, was slightly eliptical in cross-section. The engine left Darlington with a passenger train at 8.40am and on arrival at Northallerton it was detached and then coupled to a train destined for Bedale. At 10.27am, while the driver was oiling a tender bearing, an explosion demolished the entire boiler barrel, blowing all its six plates away, some in pieces, and wrecking the engine generally. The two enginemen escaped with slight injuries.

Hutchinson could not find a cause and said so in his report; there appeared, he said, to be signs of an old flaw in the angle iron that joined the barrel to the firebox but he did not consider that the explosion started there. He had to accept evidence that he was given about the safety-valves; they were, he was told, adjusted to a pressure of 110 lb/sq in and were found to be in order after the accident. The driver assured him that the boiler was well filled with water at the time so he let the case rest by saying that the explosion 'was in some unexplained way to be connected with the repairs which the boiler had just undergone', which was hardly a satisfactory conclusion. There is no mention in the report that Hutchinson inspected the torn boiler plates for himself and it may well be that Edward Fletcher took care that he did not get an opportunity to do so, because the fault was almost certainly in the boiler's ironwork. In all probability the steam pressure set up undue strains in the eliptical barrel as it tried to push the iron into a more cylindrical form, despite the resistance provided by five horizontal stays across the minor axis of 3 ft 5 in, which was 3 in less than the greater axis, these strains leading to cracks that weakened the iron until it broke.

CHAPTER 5

1871 TO 1880

A Period of Poor Maintenance

The only two explosions known to have occurred in 1871 were both in December, each causing injury to one man. The few available details from MSUA records are that on the 8th, on a colliery line at Cradley, near Wolverhampton, 'the screwed stud stays on one side of the firebox drew out' which means that one of the copper firebox sides had become so thin that the steam blew it off the copper stays, the heads of which were doubtless burned away as well. Then on the 13th on the NER at Middlesbrough a boiler barrel split open due to grooving.

Orbliston Junction station lay on the Highland Railway main line between Inverness and Keith; until October 1893, when the three-mile branch to Fochabers Town was opened, it was named Fochabers. On the morning of 4 January 1872 a 2–4–0 tender engine of the No 18 Class, built in 1863, started away from the station for Keith with an 11-wagon goods train and had gone nearly a mile when on a 1 in 350 falling gradient the boiler burst — the entire iron top sheet of the firebox casing where the steam dome was mounted was blown away from the rivets that joined it to the barrel and split into three pieces. The dome was hurled nearly 300 yards. The two footplate men were badly knocked about when the explosion flung them from the engine but a 'breaksman' working with them was killed. Although the explosion broke the engine away from its tender neither was derailed, but seven of the wagons came off the track and two of them were damaged; some of the debris evidently fell onto the line in the engine's wake.

Lt Col Hutchinson, who did not record the engine number, found that the failure of a group of stays at the top of the firebox's left-hand side caused the accident; they had almost perished from corrosion and it is rather evident that the HR's arrangements for inspecting them periodically had been decidedly slipshod. Hutchinson's report does not include any such comment, which would have been well deserved by David Jones, the company's locomotive superintendent from 1870 to 1896.

Visitors to Ennerdale Water in the Lake District are not far from Moor Row which used to be served by the Whitehaven, Cleator & Egremont Railway, a tiny system that in 1878 became a joint LNWR and Furness Railway line. On 5 February 1872 0–6–0 saddle tank No 8, built in 1862 and with a working pressure of 120 lb/sq in, had drawn up at a signal just to the west of the station shortly after 7.00am with 29 loaded coal wagons when away went the boiler barrel; the fireman was at a distance, fetching his breakfast, but the driver was killed.

Two rings formed the 13 ft boiler, each constructed of two semi-circular 7/16 in iron plates lap-jointed together. The rear ring's two lap joints had been along the barrel sides, below the water level; the top half of this ring was blown-off by the explosion, to land 50 yards away in a field, the plates having parted close to the joints because severe corrosion along them had reduced the plate thickness, to 1/16 in on the left-hand side. Lt Col Hutchinson, reporting on the incident, said that 'the reason, therefore, of this boiler bursting is very evident; the only wonder is that, considering the state of the bottom plate along the lap joint, it should not have burst long since'.

The RI papers contain only a brief note on the CR explosion on 23 March 1872 and there are no records of an inquiry having been held. All that is known of the engine concerned is that it was built in 1857 and had originally belonged to the Scottish North-Eastern Railway. On the day of the accident it was engaged assisting goods trains up the gradient from Bridge of Dun, a few miles from Montrose, to Glasterlaw which was on the main line towards Forfar and Perth. Having assisted one train it was returning light to Bridge of Dun for the next and had nearly arrived there when the boiler barrel burst, the whole of it being completely stripped from the firebox casing and the smokebox. Miraculously, the two footplate men escaped with injuries.

The people who on 16 September 1872 had taken tickets at Bray on the DW&WR and then joined the 9.00am train to Dublin must have become decidedly alarmed when on the verge of starting away 2–2–2 tank engine No 4 was more-or-less destroyed by the bursting of the boiler, which killed both enginemen instantly. After the steam had drifted away 21 bits and pieces of iron boiler plate were picked up.

Lt Col Rich was directed by the BOT to hold an inquiry but he was joined in the investigation by L.E. Fletcher, the chief inspector of the MSUA; as far as records show, this was the only occasion when the RI and the MSUA co-operated. No 4 had been built in 1855 and at the time of the incident the two balance safety-valves were set to 105 lb/sq in — the railway's engineers did not appear to know what the setting had been when the builders supplied the engine to the company. These safety-valves, which were fitted onto the cover of a manhole directly over the firebox, were remarkably diminutive; each valve closed a hole that had a cross-sectional area of 2.55 sq in, its diameter therefore being only 1.8 in which was far too small for any locomotive boiler. To make matters worse, Rich and Fletcher found that each hole had been covered by a brass plate containing a circle of small holes which reduced the 2.55 sq in to only 1.375 sq in. The boiler barrel being 10 ft long and 4 ft in diameter, such valves would hardly have been capable, with a big fire, of keeping the steam pressure to within 105 lb/sq in except when the engine was working very hard. The reason for the insertion of the plates could not be discovered but the inadequacy of the valves was not the cause of the explosion.

Although both Rich and Fletcher examined the wrecked boiler very thoroughly they could not agree about the cause. It was Fletcher's view that the boiler gave way at the manhole when the 1 in cast-iron cover, secured to the firebox casing by nuts and bolts, was torn-off and blown-away, the failure of the wrought-iron at the bolt holes causing a rent which then extended to the entire barrel. Rich disagreed: he believed on observing that the engine's crank axle was broken and the engine frame split on one side, that the main force of the explosion had been downwards, bursting the boiler at the joint between the bottom of the barrel and the firebox, where the iron was corroded to only ⅛ in. They were both of the opinion that excessive steam pressure brought about the explosion. Rich decided that the single lever which controlled both valves and projected through the weather board had been wedged by the driver, basing this conclusion on hearsay evidence that this man had at some time declared that No 4 needed 20 lb more pressure than 105 lb/sq in. It is most probable that the weakness of the manhole fastenings, the corrosion, and wedging of the safety-valves all contributed to the disaster.

An explosion on the CR at Dundee on 18 December did not apparently result in any casualties, as the MSUA made the only record of it. An engine 'boiler gave way in the barrel in the belt of plating next the firebox', which sounds very much as if a belt, fitted in the same way as on engine No 108 at Leominster, had corroded to the point of failure.

In 1873 Rich, now promoted to Colonel, paid a visit to Cardiff Dock station, TVR, where the boiler of No 14 had exploded on 15 July. A driver and fireman had taken charge of No 14 at 3.35am; it was six-coupled with inside cylinders but whether of tender or tank design is not in Rich's report. At about 3.50am, when the engine was stationary, all the boiler rings disintegrated into bits, injuring both enginemen and two other men as well. In October 1871 it had been found that the ring adjacent to the firebox was badly pitted along the bottom; the plate, originally ⁷⁄₁₆ in thick, ought to have been renewed, but instead an iron patch or 'liner' was riveted to it in an attempt to halt the corrosion. The rivet holes for the liner's attachment weakened the already defective plate even further, and it eventually split under the steam pressure.

On the same day a man was injured in a Darlington iron works, according to MSUA records, when a 'firebox of D section in plan and not stayed at the sides' exploded. Nothing more is known about the incident but the engine was clearly a very ancient relic.

South Brent, a large attractive village in Devon, has not often experienced frightening events, but the explosion of 1873 at the local station doubtless disturbed the inhabitants considerably. The main line through Brent was at that time the SDR principal route, and on 22 August the broad gauge 0–6–0 saddle tank engine *Hebe*, after arriving at Brent at 4.29pm with a goods train from Exeter, had been standing about six minutes when the boiler barrel exploded. The barrel had three rings, three iron plates to each, and the centre and rearmost rings burst open at the top; the saddle tank and the steam dome were hurled away, but miraculously the engine-men and a boy standing nearby escaped with scalds.

When Col Rich held an inquiry and learned that the boiler's equipment consisted of a water gauge, a pump and injector, but no pressure gauge, and that the injector had been out of order, he fell back on the old fallacy of the driver having let his crown sheet run dry and of steam suddenly forming when the injector became workable once more and poured cold water onto the overheated firebox. He discovered, however, that the hole cut in the barrel for the dome had not been strengthened by an angle iron ring; the locomotive's builders in Bristol had riveted the dome onto the barrel, weakening the plate by pitching the rivets too closely, and in all probability the explosion originated there.

The MSUA recorded in 1873 the explosion of another engine that ought to have been in a museum. On 1 September the locomotive was on a colliery line at Warkworth, at the extreme northern end of the Northumberland coalfield, when 'the boiler barrel gave way at the bottom and was divided into several fragments. The boiler was very old, had been fre-quently patched, and a new one to take its place had been ordered a short time previously'. Two men were injured.

The Cwmannan colliery branch on the GWR near Aberdare was part of what had begun in 1851 as the broad gauge Vale of Neath Railway which extended eastwards from Swansea to Merthyr Tydfil, with branches to Nantmelyn, Cwmannan and Aberdare; Brunel was its engineer. The Cwmannan line was about 5½ miles in length and crossed two timber viaducts called Gamlyn and Dare that continued in use until 1939 and were the very last of Brunel's timber viaducts to survive, being removed in 1947. The VofNR was absorbed by the GWR in 1865; in 1864 its gauge became mixed and in 1872 'narrow' ie standard.

0–6–0 saddle tank No 1072, running bunker-first, was drawing 66 wagons of coal from the branch terminus on 22 May 1874 when a 'D shackle' broke and 15 of the wagons were left on a short level stretch. The engine and the 51 trucks still attached descended some way down a 1 in 300 gradient before they were halted. They were then set back and the 'breaks-man' and guard were getting ready to re-couple when the copper firebox's entire crown sheet was blown-down by a violent explosion which threw the boiler and the saddle tank onto the lineside 75 yards from the engine, after striking and rebounding off one of the trucks. Both enginemen were killed.

The engine, built in 1871, had run only 52,752 miles and had not up to the day of the accident needed any boiler repairs. It was unfortunate that the boiler lacked its steam pressure gauge, which had been taken-off the previous day to be mended. William Dean, then the GWR assistant loco-motive superintendent, considered that the firebox crown had sunk due to 'over-pressure and over-heat', the boiler having been allowed to get low in water; Col Yolland however declared that 'there were no very distinct indications of overheating having taken place'.

Nevertheless, Yolland was at a loss to account for the explosion and rambled somewhat in his report: 'there is no evidence whatever to show that the safety-valves had been tampered with, by being either held or wedged down', he said, but added that 'the safety-valves and levers connected with them had been blown off the boiler'. As he found the boiler to have been generally in good order the safety-valves could have been blown-away only by a gross excess of steam pressure, a view supported by an outward bulge in the front of the firebox's iron casing. Yolland fell back on a conclusion that the crown sheet had been allowed by the enginemen to get overheated, having previously said there were no signs of this, and that 'a sudden development of steam' was produced when, after pushing the 51 wagons towards the other, the engine stopped abruptly and the water surged back onto the firebox. This was an old story and not a very good one, as the engine was in forward gear when pushing the 51 wagons up the 1 in 300 slope and any surge would have been the other way. Moreover, the explosion did not occur immediately the gap between the wagons was re-closed, because Yolland says that the guard and breaksman then obtained another shackle from the engine and were taking it towards the rear of the train when the boiler blew-up. In all probability the enginemen *did* wedge down the safety-valves before propelling the 51 wagons up the gradient and then forgot, in the absence of a pressure gauge, to release them as soon as the movement halted. It then became a matter of chance whether the firebox or the iron barrel gave way first. Why the wagons were coupled by a shackle in the first place instead of by ordinary link couplings has not been explained by Col Yolland; the wagons in use for local mineral traffic in South Wales at that time must have been in rather poor shape.

The Blyth & Tyne Railway was in trouble again in 1874, but only the MSUA appears to have been told about the incident. Three 'persons' were injured on 12 June when a locomotive went out of commission at North Shields, 'the copper firebox rent below the firedoor from wasting of the plate on the flame side'. Locomotive maintenance does not seem to have been one of the better accomplishments of the B&TR.

Monksbridge goods yard used to lie on the approach to Leeds City station, into which the L&YR had running powers. On 28 November 1874 L&YR No 189 was standing in the yard when at about 10.30pm the boiler burst, almost destroying the barrel and wrecking the motion between the engine frame. Thankfully, no one was hurt.

Col Yolland examined No 189, which began in 1847 as a four-wheeled engine with a tender; it was rebuilt as an 0–6–0 saddle tank engine in 1868, when the boiler barrel's rear ring was renewed, but not the forward ring. The explosion blew the entire forward ring off the engine. As the interior of the barrel was not inspected again after 1868, no one became aware of corrosion that reduced the bottom of this ring's $7/16$ in iron plate to about half that thickness, until the ring cracked under normal steam pressure.

Although in 1863 the S&DR, owning by this time 157 engines, became amalgamated with the NER, the system remained many years as a 'Darlington Section' and William Bouch, the S&D engineer, continued to be in charge of its locomotive affairs at least until 1875. During the afternoon of 26 February 1875 NER shunting engine No 627 was stationary at Middlesbrough on the Darlington Section when the right-hand water space of the firebox burst open; the explosion scalded the two enginemen and a guard, throwing them off the footplate. Lt Col C.S. Hutchinson found that the lower half of the firebox's right-hand copper side plate, which had wasted to only half its original thickness of ½ in, had been blown off its stays in one piece, tearing away from the foundation ring and from a line of stays about 2 ft above it, when only 12 stays out of 44 that had once been providing support finally lost what grasp they still kept. Had the boiler not burst as it did it would certainly have done so rather sooner than later where the iron casing was attached to the foundation ring, rust having reduced the plate's thickness to only ⅛ in along a length of several inches. No wonder the assembly gave way! Poor old Bouch (a brother of Thomas Bouch who was then busy building the first Tay Bridge) must have been getting inattentive to his duties as he advanced in years.

For those who have not heard of Dodworth, it lies on the line of the late MS&LR between Barnsley and Penistone. On 26 June 1875 at 2.15pm 0–6–0 No 105, although it is not recorded whether it was of tender or tank arrangement, was about to draw a coal train from the Dodworth Colliery sidings when the boiler barrel blew to pieces, the fragments being hurled in all directions. However, only the driver and the stationmaster became casualties, their injuries being slight.

The barrel, of ½ in iron plates, had horizontal seams in the form of butt joints covered by 4 in strips of ½ in iron that were, however, on only the outer sides. Corrosion had eaten half-way through one of the cover strips, weakening its inner side until it finally split. Locomotive engineers had yet to learn that butt joints need cover strips on *both* sides. Col Yolland's recommendation following his inquiry into this incident that butt joints covered with belts or strips ought to be given-up was well meant and correct with regard to annular joints in

The colliery inlet line at Dodworth where MS&LR engine No 105 blew up on 26 June 1875. (*Author*)

boiler barrels, but in the case of horizontal seams it was rather poor advice.

On 23 July 1875 NER inside-cylinder 2–4–0 tender engine No 218 was hauling a Leeds to Saltburn passenger train and had just drawn-up at the Leeds interchange station at Holbeck at about 11.00am when the boiler barrel burst and flew into pieces. Many fragments landed 200 yards away and one of the engine springs, weighing a hundredweight, was hurled over a warehouse roof. Col Yolland found that the boiler, of $^7/_{16}$ in iron plate, had been allowed to get into a most deteriorated condition; along the bottom of the barrel the plate had laminated and the inner layer had been rusted through until what remained was too weak to withhold the steam pressure. The driver escaped with a broken leg; his fireman and two other railwaymen received slight injuries.

The accident that occurred at Springhill Junction, roughly midway between Kilmarnock and Irvine on the G&SWR at about 5.45am on 28 March 1876 was horrific. 0–4–2 No 20 was running tender-first hauling a van and a carriage conveying railway workmen, when the firebox crown sheet gave way and was blown down against the tubeplate. The boiler was lifted into the air by the explosion but instead of tearing away from the engine frame it took the engine with it, the entire locomotive breaking-away from the tender and then dropping onto the two vehicles behind, which were destroyed. The driver, his fireman, a guard and a fitter who were in the van, were all killed; of ten other men in the vehicles only one escaped injury. The tender ran on ahead of the wreckage, out of control and coming to rest of its own accord a mile beyond.

Lt Col Hutchinson, after finding that the boiler's iron and copper plates had been in good condition up to the time of the explosion, concluded that shortage of water and overheating of the crown sheet had led to the accident, although he could not refrain from adding that the firebox, when weakened by overheating, 'would have been unable to resist the sudden evolution of steam caused by water washing over it, probably when steam was put on just before the explosion' (Hutchinson forgot for the moment when writing that the engine was travelling *tender-first!*) He was satisfied that the crown sheet had been free from scale deposit, but his report does not mention the condition of the engine's one water gauge, which for some reason might have deceived the enginemen.

A glance at the diagram accompanying Hutchinson's report shows that the explanation was *not* shortage of water on the crown sheet, and in any case the engine was hauling only two vehicles. With such a light load, the moderate fire that the enginemen would have maintained for the run to Irvine would have taken a fairly long time to heat a crown sheet until it became so soft as to give way, and the train had run only five miles up to the moment of the explosion. The crown was suspended from six stout roof girders, being secured to each one by seven roof bolts; an overheated crown sheet would have torn away from these bolts, or at least some of them. In fact, the crown sheet broke away from the firebox doorplate along the riveted seam and was then wrenched-off the firebox sides as, undistorted and with all the girders above it still attached, it was bent down until it almost reached the tubeplate. It is most likely that a crack had developed along the top horizontal flange of the doorplate and that the steam pressure broke the copper at this place; such cracks do not as a rule appear overnight and sound regular periodical inspection would have detected signs of the fault in time.

An engine, its number and class unrecorded, was ready to start with a goods train from West Hartlepool, NER, on 12 December 1876 when the firebox burst; the fireman was killed and the driver injured. The RI made a brief record of the accident, but there does not seem to have been a comprehensive inquiry. The copper plate beneath the firehole had wasted and become so thin, only ⅛ in in places, that eventually a large group of stays lost hold of it. On 28 March 1877 the same railway was in trouble when at about 5.30am No 510 was working a 41-wagon goods train from Darlington to Normanton. While the train was standing at Alne the two enginemen were refilling the tender tank from a water column when the boiler barrel exploded with a tremendous roar. Pieces of iron plate were scattered around, one 5ft by 3ft fragment being picked up nearly 200 yards away, but the men luckily escaped injury. Hutchinson, now promoted to Major General, found that the boiler had cracked where a 'flaw' 2ft long, which was more likely a groove, had lain along a horizontal lap seam in the nearmost of the boiler's four rings, the ⁷⁄₁₆ in iron plate being corroded until it was only ⅛ in thick.

In 1877 William Dean became the locomotive superintendent of the GWR, holding the post until 1902. On taking office he had to assume responsibility for a large number of engines, of both gauges, whose boilers had been fitted with midfeathers on the directions of his predecessor, Joseph Armstrong, and some perhaps before him by Daniel Gooch. A midfeather was an upright water-filled partition across the firebox, with sides of copper plates that were about 4 in apart, and with copper stays supporting them; it communicated with the water spaces on either side and was intended, rather wishfully, to improve water circulation, provide increased heating surface and prevent smoke.

At 8.09am on 11 September 1877 standard gauge 2–4–0 passenger tender engine No 153 was drawing the 7.40am Shrewsbury to Birmingham passenger train into Oakengates station when its midfeather burst, causing the driver's death

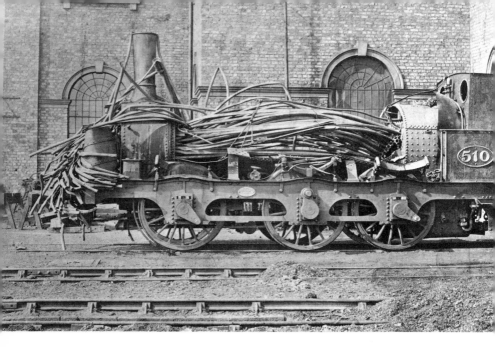

NER 0–6–0 No 510 after the explosion at Alne on 28 March 1877. (*British Engine Insurance Company*)

and the fireman to be severely scalded. One of its two ½ in copper sides was so wasted that there were not enough screw threads left for the stays to hold the plates together. All that Dean could say to Col Rich was that he would take the best course he could to prevent such a case from occurring again, by producing a tool with which the thickness of midfeather plates could be measured from time to time.

The year 1878 ran its course without any boiler explosions, until 13 September when the quiet of Nethy Bridge, GNSR, was violently shaken by the sudden failure of No 31's boiler at about 6.05pm. Nethy Bridge was the company's most westerly station, on the line that extended along the Spey valley to join the Highland Railway at Boat of Garten. The engine, of the 4–4–0 outside-cylinder tender class, was built in 1863 and its two safety-valves had Salter's balances set at 140 lb/sq in. It was working the 3.00pm mixed train from Craigellachie Junction to Boat of Garten and was standing at Nethy Bridge station when the leading ring of the three that formed the boiler barrel suddenly split along the bottom, uncurled and then soared about 200 yards before hitting the ground. In its flight it appears to have missed one of the station buildings by a small margin. All the pasengers escaped unscathed, and of four men who were on the footplate only one received serious injury — he was an engine cleaner who had intended to take an illicit footplate ride to Boat of Garten.

The boiler was of bad design. The middle ring had two lap seams, one on each side, but the foremost ring, also with two lap seams, had one along the top but the other was along the bottom which was about the worst possible place for it. Deep grooving along this seam was very evident to Maj Gen Hutchinson and it was obvious that the iron plate had parted there; 7½ years, which was far too long, had elapsed since the boiler's last internal examination.

It was also internal grooving that caused a boiler barrel to burst at Wigan, on a collliery line; the date was 19 October. the MSUA record provides the sole source of this information, but states nothing more about the incident except that a man lost his life as a result.

On 24 November a mighty explosion at Blaydon might well have been heard as far away as George Stephenson's cottage which lies about five miles to the west of the town. At about 9.10am 0–6–0 goods locomotive No 787, hauling the 5.30am goods train from Carlisle to Newcastle, had been standing about five minutes at a signal on the NER station's approach side when the boiler burst; the top of the barrel was blown 50 yards and fell into the River Tyne, smaller pieces of plate and the steam dome landing on the far bank. The enginemen escaped with scalds, severe in the fireman's case. The boiler had three rings of 7⁄16 in iron plate, two plates to each, and Maj Gen Hutchinson found that the middle ring had contained a flaw in the iron which corrosion had worsened until the plate split asunder. Even as late as 1872, when this engine was built, iron plate was not always absolutely reliable.

Passengers who had taken their places in a GWR broad gauge train that was due to leave Penzance for Plymouth at 3.50pm on 30 November, and friends on the platform who were seeing them off, had more than just a bad fright when the

Blaydon, looking west. NER 0–6–0 No 787, travelling eastwards on 24 November 1878, had nearly reached the station when the boiler exploded; some large fragments fell into the River Tyne and others on the far bank. (*Author*)

top of the engine's steam dome suddenly blew-off. Made of cast-iron and carrying two balance safety-valves, it soared high into the air, crashed through the station roof as it came down, broke a hole in the roof of an empty carriage in a siding and came to rest on a compartment floor. Fortunately there were no casualties. It would have taken only a few seconds for the boiler to discharge its entire contents through the hole in the dome, giving everyone in the station's vicinity a foretaste of the sound of the jet-propelled aircraft that would be zooming over Cornwall a century later.

The engine that was in trouble was *Iago*, a broad gauge six-coupled saddle tank locomotive; built at Swindon in 1852 and one of five in the GWR Banking Class, it was rather past its prime. By 1878 the company had nearly ceased building broad gauge locomotives, having decided that the broad gauge was not going to be retained much longer (it was actually abolished in May 1892) and the management was endeavouring to keep the existing broad gauge engines and rolling stock in a workable condition for as long as they would be required. The cast-iron dome cover was ½ in thick and 15 in diameter, and a day or two before the explosion fitters had seen steam escaping from it. Believing that the gasket between the cover and the dome was defective they renewed it — closer inspection might have shown them that the leak was actually through a crack 9 in long in the cover itself, which it seems was only just managing to hold together. The boiler's working pressure was 120 lb/sq in but when the engine was taken to the station the safety-valves were blowing-off at 100 lb/sq in. The two valves were controlled by a single lever and spring balance, and the fireman was screwing-down the wing nut to the limit permitted by a ferrule when the cover blew-off. How he escaped injury was a miracle.

Almost a year passed before the RI received news of another boiler explosion and when it came the railway concerned once again was the NER. The incident occurred on 9 September 1879 at Leamside, in Co Durham on the route between Ferryhill and Pelaw, which was known generally as the Leamside line. At about 4.50am 0–6–0 goods engine No 737 was hauling a train of 22 loaded coal wagons and a brake van, having started from Gateshead at 3.30am en route for Darlington. 500 yards or so south of Leamside station the boiler blew-up, the barrel being shattered; pieces of plate were retrieved 400 yards from the site. The two enginemen were very lucky, escaping with slight injuries and scalds.

The boiler had not been examined internally since 1872, some seven years earlier, but Maj Gen Hutchinson found little if any signs of grooving or flaws in the iron plates, except at one place, and he was satisfied that there had not been any interference with the safety-valves. The boiler however had not been attached to the engine frame by fastenings that would allow the firebox end to slide when expanding or contracting, but had been secured by the old-fashioned method of 'hanging brackets' that rigidly held the boiler onto the frame. The firebox's iron casing had been strained where the rear brackets were fastened to it, the undue stresses having induced corrosion that grooved the right-hand side until the steam pressure split the iron plate and tore the boiler barrel apart. By 1879 almost all railways had relinquished hanging brackets, which belonged to the era when locomotives had frames of timber between iron plates.

The boiler fiends travelled south to Lewes, LB&SCR, on 27

September 1879. The 2.05pm Hastings to London passenger train arrived there at 3.04pm, hauled by 2–4–0 tender engine No 174. It began to move again ten minutes later but then the boiler blew-up with a devastating explosion; the driver was killed and the fireman and train guard badly injured. Dendy Marshall's *History of the Southern Railway* illustrates No 183, another of the same class.

The copper firebox's left-hand side had given way, being blown inwards, the explosion lifting the engine off the rails and partly turning it round, derailing the tender as well. The copper plate that burst, originally $7/16$ in thick, had been wasted away by fire action until it was less than $1/16$ in in cross-section. The great William Stroudley, the company's locomotive superintendent, said 'the firebox has thin plates but not too thin; had it not blown up I think it would have stood a pressure of 200 lb/sq in', a pretty senseless observation that suggested doubts about his competency. He may have been a great designer but when he told Col Rich that he left his boiler foremen to decide for themselves when plates ought to be replaced he revealed that his general supervision was remarkably lacking — his maintenance foremen should have had a proper schedule of minimum permissible dimensions. However, Rich laid the blame for the accident on an unfortunate boiler foreman who, when examining the firebox 12 days earlier, found that the copper plate was 'a bare eighth in thickness' but nevertheless declared the firebox to be 'in good working condition'. Stroudley was not criticised at all in Rich's report.

The fiends returned to the NER in 1880, selecting Silksworth, near Sunderland, on 26 January. 0–6–0 goods locomotive No 746 came to rest on a colliery line; ten minutes later, at about 10.00am, the boiler barrel burst, the rearmost of its three rings being blown open. The fireman and train guard escaped with slight injuries; luckily for the driver, he had gone 200 yards along the line to meet another engine. The ring of $7/16$ in iron plate contained two lap seams of which, Maj Gen Hutchinson found, the lower was well below the water line and had a deep groove along it that caused the explosion.

Leamside experienced a second explosion in 1880, on 12 November at about 6.40am. Yet another 0–6–0 goods engine, No 941, was working a 40-wagon goods train from Newcastle to York and had been detained by a signal about two minutes when the boiler barrel blew to fragments. The explosion up-ended the firebox backwards onto the footplate and the entire smokebox was hurled down the embankment side. Both driver and fireman were very badly injured; severe damage to the engine included the breaking of the crank axle.

Each of the boiler's three rings was constructed of a single plate with one joint of lap form. The cause of the boiler's failure was the same as that of the Silksworth explosion; the middle ring's lap joint had been below the water level and corrosion had gouged a deep groove along it, leaving the iron plate only $1/16$ in thick in places. The boiler had not been examined internally since the engine's purchase in 1874. Maj Gen Hutchinson recommended in his report that every boiler's inner surface should be inspected after its engine had run 100,000 miles, that butt joints should be employed and that horizontal joints of one-plate rings should be above the water line. It is hardly to Edward Fletcher's credit that Hutchinson needed to write this; William Kirtley's paper which he ought to have read had been issued eight years before No 941 was acquired.

Although this book is a review of locomotive boiler explosions, one explosion of a stationary boiler became the subject of an RI investigation. The boiler in the NER Darlington works was of the Cornish type with a 16 ft outer shell 4 ft 4 in diameter and an inner fire tube 2 ft 3 in diameter; it rested lengthways along a continuous brick wall 9 in thick and 12 in high with, presumably, supports of some sort to prevent it from rolling off. Its two safety-valves, one with a weighted lever and the other with a lever and spring-balance, were set to lift at 50 lb/sq in.

On 30 April 1877 the boiler exploded, killing the boiler-man. It had been installed in 1859 and received new bottom plates in 1870; after the explosion it was found that the bottom plate at the end furthest from the fire door had given way initially, having rusted through where it had rested on the wall, until the original thickness of ⅜ in was reduced almost to nothing. The brick wall was a very bad carrier for such a boiler as it prevented the bottom from being inspected readily, and after 1870 no such examination was carried out.

A boilermaker who in the absence of directives that he ought to have had from NER officers for periodical stationary boiler inspection but which no one ever thought of issuing, examined the boiler concerned every Easter and Whitsuntide but only as far as the brickwork would allow; he had been a boilermaker 50 years, from which one infers that he *completed* his training in 1827. Major Gen Hutchinson wrote that 'the boilermaker charged with the inspection of this and other boilers at Darlington appears to me to be far too old for the satisfactory performance of so important a duty'. Shrewdly said, perhaps, but in those days men did not get an old age pension that would release them from the need to go on earning a living.

CHAPTER 6

1881 TO 1900

The Heyday of Railways in the British Isles

The period opened with a most fearsome explosion in 1881 near Thornaby-on-Tees, NER, at about 4.30pm on 26 December. 0–6–0 goods engine No 204 had hauled three wagons and a brake van along a mineral line from the direction of Middlesbrough; it was drawing up behind a stationary mineral train that had been going in the same direction. Suddenly the engine's firebox crown sheet gave way, the explosion lifting the boiler out of the engine frame and throwing it nearly 40 yards ahead. In its flight it struck the mineral train's brake van, dropped live coals onto the vehicle which immediately caught fire, and then fell upside down onto the fourth and fifth wagons beyond. A guard and a wagon inspector within the van, the two enginemen on No 204's footplate, and their own guard all lost their lives. The engine and tender, completely derailed except for one pair of tender wheels, recoiled nearly 40 yards together with the four vehicles behind it.

The state of the ruined firebox showed that the enginemen had allowed the boiler water level to fall too low, the crown sheet getting red hot as a result, but the reason for their lapse remains unknown. The boiler had only one glass tube water gauge but a fitter had checked its portways four days earlier, finding them clear, so it seems unlikely that it had been displaying a false water level; the footplate men may have mistaken the empty glass for a full one. They might have been warned in time had the single lead plug fused but not melted, its lower end having become covered with a hard incrustation. It had been in position five months, Mr Fletcher not having set out any code of periodical lead plug examinations for his engines. Maj Gen Hutchinson, after investigating the incident, and having heard from the fireman of an engine standing near No 204 that he had seen the driver working an injector immediately before the explosion, could not refrain from saying in his report that the weakened crown sheet was 'unable to resist the pressure caused by the sudden creation of steam upon water being admitted into the boiler'!

Less than two months later it was the GER's turn, at Bury St Edmunds. Class Y passenger 4–4–0 No 385 was shunting wagons at 9.00am on 10 February 1882 when the copper firebox of $7/16$ in plate burst inwards, the right-hand side giving way initially; the two enginemen and a guard were severely scalded. The explosion was violent, breaking the engine away from the tender after derailing it and lifting the engine's four driving wheels off the rails.

The firebox had been examined by a foreman boilersmith a week earlier, but although the heads of many stays were badly burned away he apparently failed to realise that immediate repairs were needed, and told Maj Gen Hutchinson that when he came out of the firebox he had concluded that a few stays would require renewal 'shortly'.

A boilersmith who examined the firebox the day before the accident said that he 'riveted the heads of about 20 stays as well as he could' where leaks had occurred, and that he did not see anything to suggest that the firebox was unsafe. The explosion occurred when the right-hand side of the firebox was stripped away from 169 stays. The plate doubtless gave way initially at a place where three adjacent stays were already broken — other stays, some with little or no head left and some that had leaked because they were loose in the plate's threaded holes, lost their grip in turn. The foreman was blamed in Hutchinson's report but one is left to ponder on the possibility that he, in turn, and the boilersmith, were being continually coerced by ruthless management into keeping the engines at work and letting repairs await the next week-end or washing out day. The GER tended to be run on such principles. The report does not state the depot that was resonsible for the maintenance of No 385, but the driver's evidence leaves little doubt that it was Cambridge.

An explosion that occurred on the NBR at 9.47pm on 1 September 1882 half-a-mile south of Dunbar resulted in an absolute catastrophe. Engine No 465 (Hutchinson's report on his investigations does not state the class or wheel arrangement) was working the 8.05pm up goods train from Edinburgh to Berwick when the boiler blew to pieces, killing the driver, fireman and a man in business as a wine and spirit merchant who was being given a ride on the footplate without authority. A large piece of the boiler barrel fell onto the opposite line where it was run over by an oncoming down goods train of 41 wagons, the engine, tender and 15 wagons being derailed, and the engine falling over onto its side. Hutchinson does not say how this train's crew fared, but after the accident they were found 'on their legs' so they evidently escaped serious injury.

No 465, built by Neilson & Co of Glasgow, was only six years old. The explosion reduced it to a mere wreck; nothing above the frame was left, the frame itself was distorted, the crank axle was broken and no doubt the connecting rods and motion were more-or-less destroyed. The boiler's working pressure had originally been 150 lb/sq in but was reduced to 140 lb/sq in during 1880. The explosion was particularly severe, one large piece of the boiler being flung nearly 500 yards; the heavy cast-iron steam dome on which the safety-valves were mounted was picked up 370 yards from the engine.

The train of 37 full and three empty wagons drawn by No 465 had halted at Dunbar where the enginemen took water — then a banking engine came onto the rear to assist it up the 4½-mile 1 in 96 climb to Grantshouse. At 9.45pm, by which time it was dark, the train was restarted but it had gone only half-a-mile or slightly more when, at a speed of 4mph to 5mph on a 1 in 200 rising gradient, No 465's boiler disintegrated.

Hutchinson could not find a reason for this explosion; his report says that 'the cause is involved in much obscurity' and could be explained 'only by a sudden generation of high pressure steam' which neither the steam pipe, presumed to be open as the train was moving, nor the safety-valves were able to deal with. However, a cause there must have been, and 'sudden generations of steam' just do not occur in boilers. To begin with the boiler, which had received general repairs at Cowlairs works only six months earlier, was not defective. A boiler inspector made his last three monthly inspection of it about ten weeks before the explosion, finding it in good order, and Hutchinson confirmed that he could not discover any serious signs of corrosion, bad material or defective stays. The lead plug, fitted only three days earlier, was intact and the boiler had not run short of water.

Only one possible solution remains, and it is a little surprising that Hutchinson did not tumble to it; the safety-valves failed to operate properly. A drawing in his report shows that the valves were of Ramsbottom's design, with a single spring in tension, and unless the driver had devised some secret means of his own for holding down Ramsbottom valves before working trains up long gradients it is unlikely that No 465's valves had been secured irregularly.

A brass finisher at St Margaret's depot, Edinburgh, said that a fortnight before the accident he found that the safety-valves opened at 132 lb/sq in and raised the blowing-off pressure to 137 lb/sq in which was three pounds lower than the boiler's working pressure. He made his adjustment by 'stretching the spring' which sounds rather odd, as if it were possible to stretch the powerful steel spring permanently without breaking it, the action would have weakened its tension on the valves; he may have meant, however, that he drew it out slightly, so increasing the tension, by applying washers to the holding-down eyebolt. He evidently left the equipment in a safe condition as far as blowing-off pressure was concerned because a driver who had been working the engine before it set off with the 8.05pm goods confirmed that the valves released steam readily at 130 lb/sq in. Whether in reassembling the spring he inadvertently made some mistake that might have made the valves liable to stick will never be known, as Hutchinson did not say in his report that he examined them.

The two safety-valves were somewhat small, being each only 2½ in diameter. Spring safety-valves all possess a disadvantage not incurred by valves that are weight-loaded —

when the valve rises as the steam pushes it open, it increases the load on the spring by stretching or compressing it a little more, until a balance is reached between the spring and the steam when the valve then hovers in a position where it is as far open as it is going to go. A safety-valve therefore needs to be of adequate diameter if the opening for the escape of the steam is to be sufficient. 3½ in valves would have been better for No 465; Gooch's *Perseus* built in 1850 had valves 4¾ in diameter. A very likely explanation for this explosion is that a very large fire had been made for the Grantshouse ascent and that it made steam faster than the two valves could set it free; the only possible alternative is that there was some small weak place in the boiler barrel that Hutchinson when examining the wreckage failed or was unable to detect.

On 13 February 1884 a GWR broad gauge engine No 2052 was shunting at Exeter when the driver noticed that water was leaking heavily from beneath the lagging on the firebox's left-hand side. He went to the engine shed, told a leading fitter and was bringing him back to the engine when they both saw the top of the firebox casing go up into the air amidst a great cloud of steam and many flying fragments. Some of the lagging sailed over the station roof, landing 150 yards away. The fireman became the only casualty, sustaining scalds as he was getting down the engine footsteps.

No 2052 was a 4–4–0 saddle tank built as No 89 for the Bristol & Exeter Railway in 1873; the GWR acquired it in 1876. The firebox casing of 7/16 in iron was in three pieces, namely two sides with a curved top to which they were connected by butt joints. These joints had each only one butt strip, riveted along the outer surfaces of the iron plates, and water had soon penetrated into the minute gaps where the plates met, corroding the strips along their inner sides and weakening them until they gave way.

The bottom of the water space around the copper firebox was curiously arranged — there was no foundation ring, the lower edges of the iron and copper plates being riveted together. This may have been to save weight; broad gauge engines must have been very heavy compared with their standard gauge counterparts.

On 5 July 1884 nearly 200 people had crowded onto the up platform at Balloch station, NBR, to watch the arrival by special down trains of a corps of volunteer troops. They took little notice of the 4.00pm up goods train from Balloch to Kipps as it was entering the station behind 0–6–0 No 417, until the engine boiler exploded, fortunately before it reached them. A lone man on the up platform was killed as the engine was passing him, another man was injured, and the engine driver was badly scalded.

No 417 was shedded at Balloch which at the time was in the charge of foreman W.P. Reid, later to become the NBR locomotive superintendent. The explosion was due to grooving along a horizontal lap joint in the barrel immediately behind the dome. The barrel's interior had last been examined early in 1880 and Reid, or whoever was responsible for boiler inspections at Balloch, should not have allowed the boiler to work as long as four years without having it examined again. However, Maj F.A. Marindin who investigated the case gave the cause as 'metal of inferior quality'.

The years 1885 to 1887 appear to have passed without any boiler explosions but in 1888 it was the NER's turn again. On 17 July 0–6–0 goods locomotive No 590 was taking a 28-wagon coal and coke train eastwards along the six-mile section between Simpasture and Stillington Junctions, on the line that was originally a branch of the Clarence Railway, and at 10.50am it had just passed Preston-le-Skerne when the boiler barrel burst, seriously injuring the driver. Not only was most of the barrel's middle ring blown away but the engine was severely damaged, the crank axle being broken. The barrel had three rings, each of two plates that were united by horizontal lap joints, one above and the other below the water line. Maj Gen Hutchinson found that the middle ring's $7/16$ in plate had become deeply grooved along the submerged joint until what iron was left could no longer withstand the steam pressure.

If ever a railway was scourged with ill luck from its inception it was the unhappy Manchester & Milford, which in 1890 possessed five locomotives to work its route mileage of 41. On 19 August in that year at about 2.15pm, No 14

Manchester & Milford Railway 2–4–0 *Carmarthen* which exploded at Maesycrugiau in August 1890 as a result of corrosion in the iron plates along the horizontal lap joints of the boiler. (*L&GRP*)

Carmarthen, displaying that somewhat ambitious number, blew-up while stationary at Maesycrugiau, fortunately without injury to anyone. Pieces of the boiler barrel flew in all directions and the steam dome was projected into the River Teify, never to be recovered. No 14 was a 2–4–0 tender locomotive, supplied to the M&MR in 1866; the boiler's working pressure was 120 lb/sq in at the outset, reduced to 100 lb/sq in during 1885. Col Rich described the boiler as 'worn out', rust having eaten half-way through the 7/16 in iron plates along the horizontal lap joints.

The Cleator & Workington Junction Railway in Cumberland was another tiny system, with a route mileage of 30, but a locomotive that blew-up at Seaton on the company's Linefoot branch on 27 November 1890 belonged to the Furness Railway which worked a good deal of the C&WJ traffic. It was 0–6–0 saddle tank No 107, one of 16 acquired when the FR acquired the WC&ER and its rolling stock. Shortly before noon it was waiting to proceed to Linefoot with its train when the middle ring of the three that formed the boiler barrel burst open. The driver, fireman and train guard were sufficiently clear at the time to avoid injury. A lap joint in the barrel had been weakened by grooving. The boiler which was 20 years old had last been examined internally five years before the explosion; Hutchinson said that 'old boilers and particularly those with lap joints should certainly be subjected to more frequent internal inspection'.

The Belfast & Northern Counties Railway was in dreadful trouble in 1897. The locomotive superintendent was Bowman Malcolm who, appointed at the age of only 22, became famous for his 2-cylinder compound engines. He continued to serve the line long after its amalgamation with the Midland Railway in July 1903 and the appointment of the NCC to manage it.

On 7 August one of his first compound engines, 2–4–0 No 58, was hauling the 3.00pm passenger train of nine carriages from Londonderry to Belfast when, on drawing close to Antrim at 5.38pm, the right-hand side of the copper firebox gave way under the steam pressure and was forced into a huge bulge. The initial cause was the breaking of 49 copper stays, but when the plate swelled out it tore away from 53 others and the boiler's contents emptied through the clear stay holes within seconds; both the enginemen were killed more-or-less outright.

The engine had been supplied by Beyer Peacock & Co in 1890; its working pressure was 170 lb/sq in. Maj Marindin learned on investigating the incident that the boiler had been repaired in the company's works at Belfast only three months earlier, when it had been tested hydraulically to 200 lb/sq in and in steam to its working pressure. The boiler plates were sound when he examined them except for the explosion damage, the Ramsbottom safety-valves were in order, and the firebox stays were of good quality copper. But 19 out of 30 stays in one group on the right-hand side were already broken, Marindin found, when the explosion occurred and nine more contained fractures; he had little doubt that the 19 had parted a few at a time over a period of many days until so large an area of copper firebox plate was left unsupported that the remaining stays could no longer hold the firebox together.

Rather surprisingly, the B&NCR did not have any arrangement for frequent examinations of boilers in service. A boiler examiner scrutinised the boiler of every B&NC engine three or four times a year, but a district foreman who inspected every working engine at weekly intervals hardly looked at the boilers, if at all. Had No 58's boiler been properly examined every time it was washed out, about once a week, the broken stays would surely have been discovered in ample time and doubtless replaced.

Bowman Malcolm was a superb designer but his running shed supervision was obviously rather loose in 1897; at the time he had only 72 engines to look after. However, he followed up the accident at once by introducing weekly 'shed day' inspections of boilers, but it is astonishing that by 1897 these had not already become standard practice on every railway. The fact is that in this period of railway history locomotive superintendents kept very much apart, disdaining to learn from or to advise one another.

The only explosion known to have occurred in 1899, the year 1898 having passed without any, was at Crynant on 13 December on the Neath & Brecon Railway, a system having 40 miles of line and eight locomotives with which to work them. During the morning 0–6–0 saddle tank No 4 was standing at the station when a large patch that had been fitted to the doorplate of the copper firebox, beneath the firehole, suddenly blew-off the stays that had been holding it. Both enginemen managed to jump off the footplate but were badly scalded.

Although the RI appointed Lt Col H.A. Yorke to investigate the accident he decided to do so in conjunction with a boiler expert, Mr Thomas Carlton of the BOT Marine Department; Carlton carried out a most detailed examination and evidently created a strong impression as he, or in one case a Mr Cranwell of the same department, was to assist similarly in every official explosion inquiry over the next 22 years.

Carlton's findings were to the point. The copper patch, about 3 ft square and $7/16$ in thick when new, had wasted until it was only $1/4$ in thick in places and was being held by stays which were so burned away that some of them were retaining the plate by only two of their screw threads. The explosion

Westerfield, GER. The boiler of engine No 522 after the explosion of 25 September 1900. (*National Railway Museum*)

Westerfield in 1981. The dmu is at the site where engine No 522 was standing when the explosion occurred. (*Author*)

forced the plate over 54 stays and partly over 12 others.

So small a railway could not afford a locomotive engineer and employed a 'foreman mechanic' to maintain the engines. This mechanic had reported to the general manager only the previous day that a group of stays in No 4's firebox needed renewal, but traffic requirements were so demanding at the time that the general manager himself decided to run the engine a few more days. His ruling was unfortunate.

Yorke was informed, amongst other things, No 4 had had a similar firebox explosion, also at Crynant, on 26 August 1897, causing injuries to both enginemen; this was the second case of an engine being involved twice in explosions. He wound up his report by saying 'it is therefore much to be hoped that the Company will find it possible to make some arrangements for causing all their locomotives to be thoroughly examined at reasonable intervals by an engineer possessing the necessary qualifications'. The obvious solution was for the N&BR to ask one of the larger railways such as the GWR to send an inspector periodically with instructions to examine and report on the company's boilers.

Westerfield is a rural station on the northern outskirts of Ipswich, where the Felixstowe branch leaves the main line to Lowestoft. On 25 September 1900 GER 0–6–0 goods engine No 522 of Class Y14 (which became the LNER Class J15) was working the 7.15am goods train of 34 wagons and two brake vans eastwards from Ipswich to Felixstowe. At about 8.45am it had drawn up at the Westerfield down home signal just to the west of the station when a violent explosion in the firebox hurled the boiler out of the engine frame, both enginemen losing their lives. The boiler rocketed over a public level-crossing, fell onto the track, rebounded, and landed on the down platform, 40 yards ahead of the engine, having knocked down a signal post, a telegraph pole and a gatekeeper's cabin. It evidently lifted the engine off the track before being torn out of the frame, as all six-coupled wheels, together with the leading and middle tender wheels, were found to be off the rails after the steam and the noise had died down.

Lt Col P.G. von Donop held an inquiry into the accident, this being his first investigation into a boiler explosion, and Mr Carlton assisted him; the report that followed was really Carlton's work, von Donop merely concurring with it. They found that the steam pressure had blown the copper firebox's entire left-hand side into the firebox, having forced it off the stays which were not of copper but bronze, a material that at this period several railways appear to have been using for firebox stays, by way of experiment. Instead of having heads within the firebox, No 522's stays projected ³⁄₁₆ in through the copper plates; the ends contained ¼ in holes about an inch in depth and had been expanded by means of a tapered drift. These stays being much more rigid than copper stays, they tended to tilt in their holes when firebox expansion occurred, so straining the screw threads in the copper plates. This lead to leaks but instead of recutting the screw threads in the plates and fitting larger stays the boilersmiths merely caulked the copper around the existing stays and re-applied their drifts; eventually the left-hand copper plate's attachment to the stays became so weak that it could no longer hold out against the boiler's working pressure.

The engine, together with its boiler, was relatively new, having been constructed at Stratford works and then sent to Ipswich on 19 September 1899 and permanently stationed there. The report does not say how many other boilers were of similar assemblage but it seems quite certain that J. Holden, the GER locomotive superintendent and a nephew of Edward Fletcher, omitted to give his running shed staff any proper instructions on how to look after his bronze stays with ends of, apparently, his own invention. The shed staff at Ipswich were left to manage the engine's maintenance for themselves and unfortunately they did not do it very well. During the year that the engine was at work 41 reports of leaks from the stay ends in the firebox were made by drivers, and a month before the explosion a fairly large bulge developed on the firebox's right-hand side, the copper plate having been forced about ⅛ in over the threads on the stays. The boilersmiths ought to have repaired the firebox by fitting larger diameter stays and cutting new threads in the copper plate, but on their foreman's instructions they merely drove the plate back into position using a heavy hammer, and then re-expanded and caulked the stays in an attempt to make them steamtight. They overlooked that their hammering pretty well destroyed what hold the screw threads still possessed, if indeed they were not already stripped. The right-hand side of the firebox was thus left in a highly dangerous condition but as it happened it was the opposite side that gave way first. When von Donop and Carlton examined the wrecked firebox they saw that the left-hand plate had also been in a bulged condition and had been merely hanging onto the stays that should have been gripping it.

The report lays most of the blame on the boiler foreman at Ipswich, which was somewhat unfair because there ought to have been at least some criticism of the local locomotive officer at Ipswich, also of Holden himself. The report does say rather patronisingly that in the course of the investigations every possible assistance was received from Holden, which tends to suggest that any attention to duties such as running shed maintenance and its supervision was deemed to be far too menial for a gentleman of so high a rank as his. The only comment on management in the report was that 'there seems to have been an opinion amongst those in charge at Ipswich that nothing worse than a leakage could occur from a new boiler', followed by a recommendation that 'it would be as well if the inspection and repairing of the boilers in the Ipswich sub-division were put in charge of an intelligent inspector', together with a hint that stay heads ought perhaps to be riveted in future.

Although it had no bearing on the accident, No 522's boiler was the first with a steel barrel to be involved in an explosion.

CHAPTER 7

1901 TO 1921

Six Historic Cases

The first boiler explosion of the twentieth century was near Knottingley on the L&YR. Mr H.A. Hoy, the company's chief mechanical engineer, had introduced a series of 0–8–0 tender goods engines — their Belpaire boilers, working at 175 lb/sq in, were 25ft 3in long and 4ft 10in diameter, the fireboxes being almost 8ft in length. One of these, No 676, was hauling 52 loaded coal wagons and a 20-ton brake van towards Goole on 11 March 1901, travelling tender-first. At 6.50pm it was on the approach embankment that led to the Aire & Calder Canal bridge, nearly three miles from Knottingley, when the whole of the firebox's left-hand side and part of the crown sheet gave way with a tremendous explosion; the blast of escaping steam hurled the entire boiler out of the engine frame, pitching it onto the side of the line from where it toppled into a field. Both enginemen were killed instantly. Several yards of permanent way were battered to pieces, causing the derailment of the engine and 24 of the wagons, ten of which rolled down the embankment. The explosion cracked the engine's left trailing wheel and bent the 7½ in steel trailing axle. The entire incident was almost a repetition of what had happened at Westerfield six months earlier, except that No 676 was moving at the time.

At the BOT inquiry held by Major E Druitt of the RI with Mr Carlton's assistance, it was learned that at the inquest Mr Hoy had attempted to claim that the explosion was the result of an unduly low water level in the boiler, the firebox crown sheet becoming bare when the engine ran onto the 1 in 159 rising gradient that led to the bridge, but Carlton would have none of this as the engine had been on the incline only some 30 seconds when the explosion occurred; the crown sheet and the corners where the side plates joined it would not have become red-hot in so short a time.

Mr T.H. Riches, the locomotive superintendent of the TVR, and it would seem one of Hoy's close pals, gave evidence, most of which was nonsense. It was his view, too, that shortage of water had led to the explosion, the crown sheet giving-way first and the rupture extending down the left-hand side. He admitted that he had not seen No 676's boiler; damage that he observed in a photograph had in fact been caused when the somersaulting boiler struck the ground.

Carlton soon revealed what had been wrong. A group of 'bronze' stays on the firebox's left-hand side had failed initially — a few were already broken and others partly cracked *within the copper plate* before the explosion. All the firebox stays were of an alloy of Hoy's own invention, the mixture's proportions being 31 of copper, 19 of zinc and 0.187 of iron. He claimed that it was stronger than copper and that 'perhaps' it was more elastic and giving when the stays had to endure the greater expansion of the copper firebox compared with that of the steel casing. It turned out that the alloy possessed very little elasticity which was mainly why the stays cracked, and as for being stronger Hoy's plea was quite futile as the effectiveness of the stays depended mainly on the strength of the screw threads in the weaker metal which was the copper. A final pathetic suggestion by Hoy that a colliery shot-firer's explosive cartridge had got into the coal received scant attention.

As in the case of the Westerfield engine, the stays had been leaking in the firebox, a little at first and then more so as the weeks went by, one fireman saying he had never seen a boiler leak so badly. Boilersmiths' attempts to stop the leaks by hammering the stay heads were so excessive that they probably caused some of the cracks. Moreover, the water spaces were only 2½ in wide in their lower parts. The water circulation was reduced, and as a result the stays became overheated, in which state they lost nearly 50% of their tensile strength. The firebox's collapse was the result of all these defects combined.

How, with 39 other boilers of the same type in use, Hoy explained all this to his directors remains unrecorded. He had been the L&YR CME since 1899 and held the post until 1904.

No more explosions occurred until 1906 when the L&YR again ran into bad luck. On 9 April at 10.21pm, 2–4–2 tank engine No 869 was hauling the 9.30pm passenger train from Stockport to Colne and had just passed through The Oaks station, about 2½ miles north of Bolton, when its firebox crown sheet burst downwards off its vertical stays. Mr Carlton virtually conducted Druitt's investigation and then wrote the report; Druitt, by this time a lieutenant colonel, merely certified it. The Belpaire boiler supported its copper firebox by 150 vertical iron stays that were screwed through the copper crown sheet with nuts beneath it; 57 of them broke flush with the crown sheet underside, all the nuts falling into the fire, and an area of the sheet about 3ft square was pushed down in a huge bulge, fortunately without splitting. The steam at 170 lb/sq in roared through the 57 one-inch stay holes, scalding the driver badly, and the fireman was injured when he fell from the footplate. The train was stopped by the guard.

There was no doubt about the cause. Carlton found scale ⅜in thick on undamaged parts of the firebox top and round the vertical stays. It was evident that this covering had deprived the crown sheet and its stays of water to such an extent that they became severely weakened by the heat of the fire until four stays broke initially, the other 53 then parting in quick succession as the extending bulge wrenched them sideways. The practice at Colne was for boilers of tank engines allocated there to be washed-out every eight days, which provided adequate intervals. Carlton was told that No 869 had been in the shed for this purpose only five days before the accident. It may well have been in the shed but whether its boiler was properly washed-out on that occasion seems questionable, and Carlton's discovery of 72lb or about ⅔-cwt of loose scale in the water spaces around the firebox makes it doubtful whether any washing-out was done at all. Indeed, this evidence suggests two or three weeks of continuous working since the engine was last in the hands of a boiler-washer.

The shed foreman was required to satisfy himself that after the boiler had been washed-out it was clean inside, and he should have inspected the interior using a light steel rod with a burning paraffin-soaked rag on one end to provide illumination; three plug holes on either side of the boiler would have afforded him a clear view across practically the entire crown sheet but his insistence that he looked through them and found the boiler scale-free is difficult to accept. It so happened that a boiler inspector examined this engine on the same occasion but he did not look at the firebox top at all. His reason, he said, was that he had found the inside of the firebox in good order and so assumed everything else to be shipshape; it is surprising that Carlton did not criticise him, the way in which he scrutinised the boiler being hardly to his credit.

Whether the shed foreman was not looking after his engines properly or whether he was having difficulties in getting all the necessary work to his engines done on their 'shed days' is something that Carlton and Druitt have not commented on in their report.

In the 1930s the motive power officers of the LMSR were insisting in their drive for maximum locomotive availability that both the boiler washing and all the necessary running repairs were to be completed on a single shed day. They overlooked, either by intention or because they had lost touch with reality, that fitters cannot work beneath an engine when streams of dirty cold water are cascading from the boiler's mud holes and plug holes. It is quite likely that similar demands, impossible to meet, went out to the foremen and others in charge of engine sheds on the L&YR in 1906, and that to enable fitters to attend to connecting rods or axle-boxes on shed day, boiler-washing was sometimes postponed. Colne depot, being very much an outpost of the system, was probably not being visited often enough by officers and inspectors from headquarters. George Hughes, who became cme of the L&YR in 1904 (and later on the first cme of the LMSR), ought to have remembered that outposts sometimes need more surveillance than larger and centrally-placed establishments.

The report on this explosion is the only one amongst the RI that attributes the collapse of a firebox to unjustifiable accumulations of scale. Whether some of the earlier firebox explosions ought to have been ascribed similarly must remain unknown, but it is likely that in some cases neglected washing out played at least a part.

Negligent supervisors usually received very little sympathy from Mr Carlton. At about 3.00am on 25 September 1907 the people of Wath-on-Dearne were violently disturbed when the boiler of H&BR engine No 109 blew up, causing the driver's death. Wath is in South Yorkshire and a single line H&B passenger branch terminated there at a very small station, the branch's main purpose being to serve collieries. Carlton's investigations, made on behalf of Lt Col von Donop, revealed a shocking state of affairs.

No 109 was an 0–6–2 tank engine, one of nine in the company's F2 class, originally with a working boiler pressure of 170 lb/sq in. It was allocated to the company's depot at Cudworth, and shortly before the accident it was attached to a goods train that it was to haul from Wath to Wrangbrook. The fireman was on his way back from the signal box, bringing the train staff for the journey, when the engine's copper firebox suddenly yielded to the steam pressure. The whole of the left-hand side of the firebox was blown down onto and then through the grate, being forced beneath the foundation ring, torn off it, and flung a distance of 40 yards, the rear of the engine being at the same time lifted several feet off the track, falling back onto the ballast. A group of about 30 stays near the bottom of the firebox's left-hand side had failed.

Carlton found that the riveted heads of these stays had been burned away until the stays themselves had become too short, their ends lying *within* the copper plate. Moreover, they had been hammered and caulked so frequently in attempts to keep them steamtight that the screw threads had been strained and damaged until the plate was no longer supported properly. As in previous cases of this kind, a small number of adjacent stays gave way first and then the copper plate slipped or was pulled off the remaining stays, tearing away from the tube plate and back plate at the same time.

The engine had been purchased from a building firm by the H&BR in 1901 and had received its first general repair at Springhead Works in 1905, after which it was maintained continuously at Cudworth. By March 1907 the Cudworth shed foreman realised that the stays were getting into poor condition but instead of renewing them he had the boiler's working pressure reduced to 160 lb/sq in by re-adjustment of the Ramsbottom safety-valves. Shortly before the accident a boilersmith warned the foreman that it was time that No 109 went back to Springhead for repairs — the foreman preferred to wait until No 106 could be sent from the works to replace No 109, which was a most regrettable decision. He was held entirely responsible for the explosion.

Nevertheless, the H&BR had only 116 engines at that time and Mr Stirling, the company's locomotive superintendent and a son of the great Patrick Stirling of Doncaster, ought to have been able to keep in touch with the general affairs of his department without much difficulty. It seems most odd that No 109's worsening condition was not brought to his notice by the Cudworth foreman but it appears to have been kept from him. Stirling may have been one of the many unapproachable autocrats who occupied principal officers' posts in that era of railway history, but it is much more likely that he was under pressure from his directors to manage his department with forceful economy and that his foremen knew this all too well. His career apparently remained unaffected by the Wath incident; he held his post of locomotive superintendent from the opening of the H&BR in 1885 throughout the company's entire life until it was absorbed by the NER in April 1922. No 109 was repaired and became LNER No 2490, lasting until 1936 or thereabouts.

On 21 April 1909 the good people who dwelt in the southerly parts of Cardiff were startled shortly after midnight by a shattering explosion which occurred at the docks locomotive depot of the Rhymney Railway. No 97 had been taken there because the injectors would no longer operate and two men were engaged in prising up a few firebars and scraping the burning coals off the grate and out of the ashpan when the entire copper crown sheet was blown down into the firebox, the boiler then being torn off the engine frame and hurled about 45 yards. Both the men were killed and also another man who happened to be a few yards away at the time;

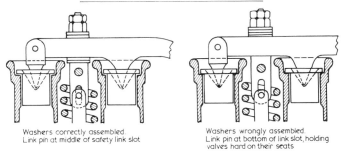

Washers correctly assembled.
Link pin at middle of safety link slot

Washers wrongly assembled.
Link pin at bottom of link slot, holding
valves hard on their seats

two more men were injured.

Lt Col Druitt was directed to hold an inquiry, but Mr Carlton brought all the facts to light. The engine was an 0–6–2T, a type that was popular for short-distance coal traffic in South Wales as it was on the H&BR, but with a saddle tank instead of the more common side tanks. The boiler was only eight months of age and in good well-kept condition; its working pressure was 160 lb/sq in, but its Ramsbottom safety-valves had been set to lift at 145 lb/sq in.

No 97's fire had been kindled eight hours or so before the accident and by 11.00pm the steam gauge was registering 110 lb/sq in. A driver who took charge at 11.30pm noticed that the gauge needle was standing at 200 lb/sq in; feeling apprehensive, he attempted to test the safety-valves but could not move the lever either way. He told a fitter what he had seen and this man looked at the gauge and then reported to the shed foreman that it was registering incorrectly. Without going to see for himself, the foreman told the fitter that the gauge was in order and that the engine was to take up its working.

The engine was run about a mile along the line but then the driver could not get the injectors to work, and so had no option but to return the engine to the depot. While various men were trying unsuccessfully to manipulate the injectors the water gauge glasses burst, first one and then the other. Finally it was decided to drop the fire, but the boiler blew-up before this was done.

Although the boiler fittings were all badly damaged as well as the boiler itself, Mr Carlton soon discovered the cause of the disaster — the safety-valves had been wrongly assembled and were unable to open. On the previous day, when the boiler was being washed-out, a fitter was detailed to repair the joint where the safety-valve mounting was attached to the boiler, and the work involved the removal of the mounting from its place. The fitter found it necessary first to take off the safety-valve lever in order to lift the mounting clear of the saddle tank, and this required the uncoupling of the upper eyepiece from the safety links. On reassembling these parts the fitter failed to notice that he was not replacing the eyepiece washers as they had been before and he left the engine with the two valves held hard on their seats by the safety links instead of by the coil spring.

The reason for the injectors' failure to operate was that the steam pressure had risen far beyond that at which they were designed to work, although the pressure gauge did not display a figure above 200 lb/sq in because a stop was holding the needle at that position. The boiler was almost at bursting point when the men decided to drop the fire and the stirring of the coals on the grate evidently produced a spurt of heat that increased the steam pressure until the boiler could no longer contain it.

Someone suggested to Carlton — his report does not say who — that the boiler had become short of water, that an injector had been made to work and that the water, flowing over the overheated firebox, caused a sudden generation of steam which brought about the explosion. Carlton disposed of this aged concept once and for all. His report says that:

> the theory advanced is a very old one, and has been very frequently put forward to account for boiler explosions, but in the explosion reports dealt with under the Boiler Explosion Act, which number upwards of 1,800, I am not aware of a boiler having burst from this cause. An interesting and valuable experiment was made by the Manchester Steam Users' Association on a Lancashire boiler, in which

the flues were made red hot, and the feed water was sprayed *over* the red hot parts to obtain the greatest effect of accumulated pressure. The safety-valves were blowing off at the time the water was sprayed on the red hot flues, but no increase of pressure whatever occurred, in fact, the pressure immediately began to fall after the feed was put on, and in ordinary boilers, if the safety valves are of the usual proportions, and operative, there is no reason to think they would fail to carry off any pressure so generated without undue accumulation.

The way in which steam was raised and the engine despatched from the depot after the safety-valves had been dismantled and put together again came in for Carlton's keenest criticism. The fitter concerned, or some other competent man, ought to have satisfied himself that the safety-valves lifted when the boiler's maximum working pressure was reached, but it seems that RR did not have any code of procedure that required such a test after safety-valve assembly and adjustment. This was another example of poor running shed organisation that hardly contributed to the reputation of Mr C.T. Hurry Riches, the company's locomotive superintendent, and a son of the 'Taff Vale' Hurry Riches who has been mentioned earlier. He had only 110 engines in all to look after.

Three more years passed and then Tunbridge Wells on the SE&CR, became the scene of an incident. 4–4–0 No 216 left Tonbridge at 5.53am on 29 April 1912 with four empty bogie carriages and was within a mile-and-a-half of Tunbridge Wells when the firebox roof collapsed; the enginemen escaped with their lives but were badly injured by falling or jumping from the footplate.

Mr Carlton's inspection, made in partnership with Maj J.W. Pringle of the BOT, revealed at once that the boiler had been short of water, the level of which had fallen to about four inches below the crown sheet. The fireman's insistence that the water had been standing three-quarters of the way up the gauge glass was not accepted. The engine was running tender-first at the time on a rising gradient of 1 in 100, causing the water level to be lower at the firebox end; the fireman should have anticipated this before coming to this incline and kept the water level adjusted accordingly.

There are no records of any boiler explosions during the years of the 1914–18 War but the Railway Inspectorate's investigation work was reduced considerably throughout this period and the statistics that were compiled or preserved are scanty. On 11 November 1921 the pleasant Derbyshire town of Buxton was shaken at 12.45am by a frightful explosion at the LNWR station. 0–8–0 tender locomotive No 134 had just begun to draw a 34-wagon goods train from a siding en route for Oldham when the boiler literally blew to pieces, the firebox, smokebox, the barrel full of twisted tubes, and odd bits of plate being flung in all directions, some landing 200 yards away or more. The engine itself was pitched off the track and both trailing wheels were torn away and tossed into the air, one of them landing on a wagon of coal. Both the enginemen lost their lives.

The incident was practically a repetition of what had happened at Cardiff in 1909. The Ramsbottom safety-valves, of rather unusual design with a coil spring in compression instead of tension, were defective and had failed to open. Major G.L. Hall held an inquiry, along with Mr H. Cranwell. No 134 was a four-cylinder compound engine with a working pressure of 200 lb/sq in. By the end of World War I most of Britain's railways were sadly behind with their locomotive repairs and the LNWR was sending engines to be overhauled by engineering firms who were no longer getting orders of any size from the army and navy and were seeking work for their employees. In 1920 No 134 went to a works in Glasgow where it was given extensive repairs and it was returned to the company in July 1921.

The two safety-valves were in cast-iron columns. Each valve, of gunmetal and with three webs, rested on and within a gunmetal bush which provided its seat; these bushes fitted firmly within the columns. The Glasgow mechanics left the valve webs with very little play in the bushes. They were apt to be tight when the boiler was cold but, gunmetal having about twice the coefficient of expansion of cast-iron, they became very tight indeed when the valves were heated by the steam. It happened to be exceptionally cold in the early hours of 11 November and the low air temperature tended to hold back the expansion of the cast-iron, making the fit of the valves tighter still and preventing the boiler's steam pressure from pushing them open. The possibility of such a failure ought to have been known to Hewitt Beames, who on 1 December 1920 succeeded C.J. Bowen Cooke as CME of the LNWR; in a paper read at the Institution of Mechanical Engineers in July 1877 on *The Construction of Safety Valves* the author advised that 'a seating should never be in the form of a brass bush inserted in a cast iron cover, owing to the difference of expansion of the two metals'.

The tight fit of the valves was the main cause of the accident but there were other features. Between July and 11 November the engine ran only 2,600 miles, but during that period several drivers reported that the steam pressure gauge was defective — one repair entry said 'steam gauge goes all round' and another 'gauge wants changing — registers 300lbs'. The gauge was changed several times, but on each occasion it was the gauge that was suspected; it did not occur to anyone to question the reliability of the safety-valves. The last replacement of the gauge was at Buxton on the day before the explosion but gauges could be changed only when the engine was not in steam, the pipe connecting the gauge to the boiler not having a shut-off cock, which is rather surprising. It was not possible to replace a suspected gauge with another on the spot in order to compare readings. Moreover, the LNWR depots were not provided with test gauges and with fittings for connecting them to some readily accessible part of a boiler such as a water gauge drain cock. A test gauge check would have revealed the true state of affairs and it is quite astonishing that the company's shed foremen had not been issued with these important pieces of equipment. After the accident a boiler of the same type was tested hydraulically to ascertain what pressure it would withstand; it began to give way at about 600 lb/sq in and it may be assumed that No 134's boiler blew-up when the steam reached a similar pressure.

CHAPTER 8

1921 TO 1962

The Era of the Big Engine

The Buxton explosion was the last among the pre-grouping companies, also the last boiler barrel explosion, those that followed being cases of collapsed fireboxes. The 1923 amalgamations set up the 'Big Four', whose chief mechanical engineers established such stringent schedules of works and running shed boiler and maintenance that almost 19 years elapsed before another explosion occurred on a British railway. The good record ended on 10 September 1940 near Carstairs, on the LMSR.

Carstairs is on the Glasgow to Euston main line, about half-way along the almost continuous 50-mile climb to the 1,014 ft Beattock Summit. Southbound trains have to start climbing shortly after leaving Glasgow until reaching Craigenhill, from where they descend a few miles, passing through Carstairs, before the climb to Beattock starts again. The train concerned, of 16 coaches, was the 10.00am from Glasgow Central to Euston hauled by streamlined 4–6–2 Coronation No 6224.

The 10.00am departure from Glasgow was prompt but with the train in the charge of a driver and fireman who did not normally work long-distance expresses and had entered No 6224's cab with only three minutes to spare — the regular men had been delayed. Although both properly qualified, they had never worked together before, and the fireman had never previously fired a Coronation Pacific. This was not at all to their discredit as the achievement of anything involves doing it for a first time.

Unfortunately the fireman did not provide enough fire for the engine's needs and the steam pressure soon began to fall. The two men succeeded in getting the train over the Craigenhill summit but as they were coasting down towards

Carstairs the firebox suddenly gave way. The driver managed to stop the train, but he and the fireman were terribly burned and scalded by the huge discharge of high temperature steam, and later in the day the fireman died.

In 1900 the RI team of inspecting officers had been strengthened by the engagement of four employment inspectors, whose duties were at first confined to the investigation of accidents to railway personnel. They were not asked to conduct the inquiries into any of the boiler explosions that occurred between 1900 and 1921. By 1940 all the employment inspectors were men who had either been locomotive shed-masters or had held posts in locomotive works; with their practical training and experience they were far better qualified to investigate boiler explosions than any of their predecessors, and the Carstairs accident was examined by Mr J.L.M. Moore, the senior inspector.

Mr Moore found that the boiler had run short of water until the crown sheet had become red hot but the damage was confined to a small area; a piece only about 30 in by 12 in blew out of the copper plate. Nevertheless, the whole crown sheet had bulged down between the roof stays by as much in places as an inch. Had the entire crown sheet given way instead of a relatively small area of plate the magnitude of the explosion might well have completely wrecked the engine and brought catastrophe to the 16-coach train as well. In their efforts to keep up the steam pressure the two enginemen had evidently spared the use of the injectors, failing in their efforts to avoid delaying the train to watch the water gauges; they also forgot that after passing the Craigenhill summit there would be less water on the crown sheet than before.

During World War II consignments of 2–8–0 tender goods engines, built in the USA and complying with Britain's loading gauge, were shipped to British ports. They were of American design but had both Westinghouse and vacuum brake equipment. They were intended for military railway operations on the European continent as soon as the allied forces obtained a foothold there. The first batch arrived in Britain late in 1942 and altogether 756 of these locomotives were landed. 398 were loaned to the British companies and augmented the country's locomotive stock until they were needed by the US Army, all of them being handed back by October 1944. They were very good engines and made a tremendous contribution to Britain's motive power needs during the war years.

The boilers each had one water gauge, which was on the fireman's side of the cab, and three test cocks on the driver's side. These gauges were of the Klinger reflex type, and remarkably different from those fitted to British locomotives. Instead of the water being within a slender and vulnerable glass tube it was contained in a vertical case of square cross-section having three thick brass sides; a stout glass plate provided the fourth side. This plate, flat on its outer side, had vertical prisms cut along the inner side which made the water look black from without and gave the steam space above the water a silvery appearance. It was thus very easy to observe the water levels and there was virtually no risk of such a gauge bursting. The upper, lower and drain cocks for testing water levels were not plug cocks, as on a British locomotive, but were of the screw-valve type. The upper cock was positioned high above the gauge fitting, being connected to it by a copper pipe, and its wheel located on the driver's side of the footplate, was on the end of a rod nearly 2½ ft long and having a universal joint. This cock could thus be shut, if it needed to be closed suddenly, without risk of a man getting his hands scalded. It was a most excellent gauge and it seems odd that although the prismatic or reflex system was by no means new it had not been introduced on British locomotives; British tradition and conservatism, it seems, required the design of *Rocket*'s gauge to be perpetuated.

An explosion at Honeybourne on the GWR was the first of three that occurred on one of these USA engines within a period of nine months, and in each case the cause was that the footplate staff, lacking adequate instruction, did not properly understand the operation of the American water gauge.

Honeybourne station, in Worcestershire, gave its name to four adjacent junctions that occurred where the Oxford to Evesham line crossed and was connected by spurs to the line between Stratford-on-Avon and Cheltenham. The 2.35pm goods train from Banbury, hauled by USA engine No 2403 and on its way to Margam in South Wales via Leamington and Stratford was approaching the East Junction at 11.55pm on 17 November 1943 when the engine's firebox crown fell in. Despite the huge discharge of high temperature steam the driver sustained only slight scalds but the fireman was gravely scalded and died some hours later.

The boiler, with a working pressure of 225 lb/sq in, had a steel firebox 7 ft long and nearly 6 ft wide; the tube plate was of ½ in steel, the crown, sides and doorplate being ⅜ in thick. The crown sheet, supported by 238 iron stays, had the slope typical of most 20th century engines; it was three inches higher at the front than at the back and had two fusible plugs of which neither could be seen from the footplate.

The explosion caused the crown sheet to tear away from its roof stays, having been overheated and weakened due to shortage of water in the boiler. It was forced down some 19 inches, pulling in the firebox front, back and sides and ripping them off their stays. None of the firebox plates split, but the scores of open stay holes and the top row of superheater tube holes released all the steam and water within a few seconds. It was found that the enginemen had been misled by the water gauge. The steam valve of the upper fitting was only slightly open, causing the water to stand at a much higher level in the gauge than in the boiler. The gauge's lower portway was more-or-less level with the middle of the sloping crown sheet, and when at the Ministry inquiry held by Mr Moore the driver said that he had seen the water swirling behind the gauge glass Moore at once realised that the water level had dropped until the gauge's lower passage was partly occupied by steam, when the front half of the crown sheet would have been dry.

The four main line railway locomotive running super-intendents had observed as soon as the USA engines arrived that the water gauges' steam cocks differed from British cocks and put a conspicuous plate beneath every upper cock worded 'This valve to be always in the open position'. They had not appreciated that the valve, which needed only one turn of its handwheel to shut it completely, required to be *fully* open, and that even if slightly closed a serious false reading was

Thurston. USA 2–8–0 No 2363; view inside the firebox at the collapsed crown sheet and the three broken water tubes. (*British Railways*)

View through the firehole of USA 2–8–0 No 2363 showing the crown sheet after the explosion of 12 January 1944 had forced it down. (*British Railways*)

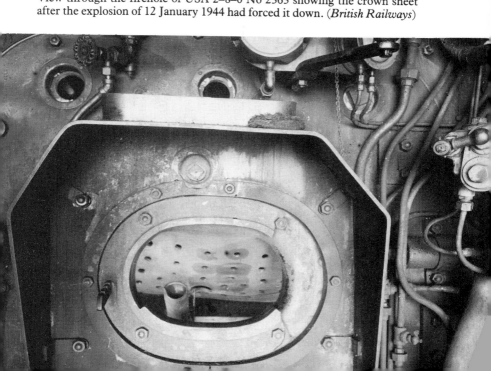

rendered. In fact, false levels varied with the extent of the closing of the valve, and could with the valve shut be as much as twelve inches above the water level in the boiler.

After the accident No 2403's steam valve spindle was found to be slightly bent, tending to bind in the gland's packing-nut as a result. The driver, and another driver who had worked the train as far as Leamington, had tested the steam valve by closing it and then opening it as far as it would go. Unknown to them, however, they had not opened it fully but only to where the bent spindle permitted.

In every British running shed all the drivers and firemen were at once given instructions and demonstrations that showed how important it was that USA water gauge steam cocks were fully open. (The author was one of the many shedmasters who had this duty to carry out.) Every plate was changed to read 'This valve must be full open'.

It was hoped that no more such explosions would occur, but it was not to be. At 12.40am on 12 January 1944, USA engine No 2363 hauling a freight train from Ipswich to Whitemoor was approaching the LNER station at Thurston, near Bury St Edmonds, when the firebox crown sheet gave way in the same manner and due to the same cause as at Honeybourne, except that the explosion was more severe, the firebox top being bulged down at least three feet. The fireman was blown from the engine, luckily escaping with severe bruises and some burns. The firehole door was blasted off its hinges, striking and breaking one of the driver's thighs. The train ran on about a mile without anyone at the controls, passing Thurston station and coming to rest on a slightly rising gradient.

Mr Moore investigated the incident, and when he tried the water gauge steam valve he found it to be so stiff towards its fully-open position that the wheel needed both hands to turn it — the enginemen had evidently believed it to be properly open when in fact it was not. Shortly after the Honeybourne incident notices had been posted at Ipswich, where the driver was stationed, instructing enginemen that the test cocks on USA engines were for the purpose of checking water levels and that it was a driver's duty to see that both water gauge and test cocks were in order. Moore blamed the driver for the

USA 2–8–0 No 1707 after the explosion in South Harrow tunnel on 30 August 1944 which blew the crown sheet down into the ashpan; the wrecked ashpan side was bent over a wheel. (*British Railways*)

The crown sheet of USA No 1707 lying in the bottom of the firebox. (*British Railways*)

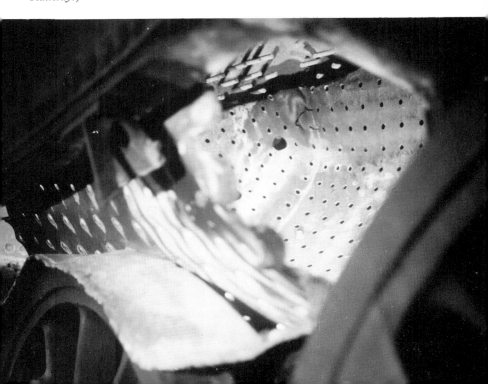

accident in that he did not take sufficient care to ensure that the valve was completely open, or to use the cocks. If it be thought that this was unduly hard it should be remembered that there were many ex-GER engines at Ipswich which were similarly fitted with a single-glass tube gauge and a trio of test cocks; the driver had no reason for being unfamiliar with the arrangement.

The third accident occurred on 30 August 1944 when USA No 1707 was hauling a goods train from Neasden to Woodford along the former GCR main line. The train left Neasden goods yard at 3.30am but fifteen minutes later it had gone only about four miles and the engine was about half-way through the 200yd South Harrow tunnel, between Sudbury Hill and Northolt Park stations, when water shortage caused the firebox top to cave in. This explosion was very severe, the crown sheet being forced down through the grate into the ashpan; terrible scalds caused the deaths of both enginemen.

After the accident a locomotive inspector found the water gauge steam valve fully open; it was in good working order and so were all the other boiler fittings. How it came about that these two enginemen allowed their firebox top to become dry remains a mystery, but in Moore's opinion they read the gauge incorrectly in the darkness, believing that it showed water up to the top of the glass. Use of the test cocks now and then might have revealed their mistake in time.

It is appropriate to mention that apart from the Thurston and South Harrow accidents and as far as the RI's records show no boiler explosion occurred on the LNER, and none at all on any LNER engines from the time of the company's formation in 1923 until the last one was withdrawn from British Railways service.

Once again, it was water shortage in the boiler that caused the next explosion to occur, on 23 April 1945 on the Southern Railway. Lord Nelson No 854, after general repairs in the Eastleigh locomotive works only a month earlier, set out from Bournemouth at 11.02am with a 14-coach train. It had travelled about 12 miles and was between Hinton Admiral and New Milton when the firebox top gave way. Steam burst with explosive force through the firehole, hurling the fireman into

Looking into the firebox of SR Lord Nelson 4–6–0 No 854 after the crown sheet had burst inwards on 23 April 1945 between Hinton Admiral and New Milton. (*British Railways*)

the tender with appalling scalds that caused his death three days later. The driver escaped very lightly, but the steam compelled him to scramble onto the running plate outside the cab, from where he managed to apply the brake and stop the train.

The water level had dropped about three inches below the firebox's highest point, and due to severe overheating the crown sheet was rent and was bulged down a foot or more, having forced the nuts off 196 of the roof stays. It was evident that the heat of the fire had brought the crown sheet to a very plastic state, there being impressions in it left by the roof stay nuts, some ¼ in deep.

The engine had been prepared for work by two other locomotive men who, after running it light to Wimborne and returning with a set of coaches, then attached it to the 11.02am London train. The driver noticed that the top of the water was not visible in the glass tube of either of the two water gauges but accepted his fireman's word that it was out of sight somewhere in the upper gauge fittings. They were relieved at about 11.00am by the driver and fireman who were to work the train, who also assumed that the water level which was still out of sight was above the upper packing nuts. It was obvious to Mr Moore, who investigated the incident, that the boiler's water level had been below the range of the gauge glasses all morning and he blamed the train driver for what happened — on taking charge of No 854, this man could have checked the water level by testing one of the gauges, during the few minutes before the train started, but did not do so. This was a most unusual lapse for a main line driver but the two enginemen who had previously had No 854 were also very slack, they too having failed to make the simple water gauge test.

The SR was again overtaken by a boiler disaster two years later. On 15 October 1947 there was a dreadful explosion at Hither Green locomotive depot. 0–6–0 goods engine No 1572 of a class introduced in 1900 had been placed on a track outside the engine shed and at 9.15am a driver and fireman began to prepare it for working a goods train to Old Oak Common. A few minutes before 10.00am, when both men were in the cab, the firebox top gave way, the steam discharging with such force that it lifted the engine completely off the rails, and the tender all but its rear wheels, dropping them onto the sleepers and ballast. By some miracle neither man was killed, but the fireman was blown off the footplate with very severe scalds; burns and scalds sustained by the driver were less serious.

The copper firebox's flat crown was carried by eight longitudinal roof girders to which it was held by 112 mild-steel 1 in stays. The explosion occurred when all these stays yielded, due to their shockingly corroded condition immediately above the crown sheet; they were screwed into the girders and had nuts beneath the crown but had become so thin that they could no longer keep the firebox in place.

That the boiler was in such a bad state was due to extraordinary lapses in the Ashford works during July 1944 when the engine received general repairs. A boiler shop foreman examined the boiler and wrote 'roof stays bad' in a notebook, along with comments on other parts needing repair.

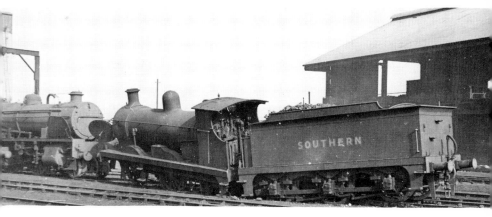

Bottom SR class C 0–6–0 No 1572 lying derailed after the firebox explosion on 15 October 1947 had lifted it off the track at Hither Green depot. (*British Railways*)

Middle The wreckage beneath the right-hand side of No 1572 after the Hither Green explosion. (*British Railways*)

Topright Inside No 1572's firebox; looking up at the roof girders from which the explosion had ripped the crown sheet and had partly torn down the right-hand side of the firebox. (*British Railways*)

Top left Some of No 1572's roof girder stays on display; they were almost corroded through. (*British Railways*)

The work items that were required were then passed verbally by another foreman to a chargeman, all but the renewal of the roof stays which was overlooked. The work carried out by the boilersmiths was not checked against the notebook. The boiler was put back onto the engine and allowed to leave the shops with the defective roof stays untouched. Anyone would have thought that by the middle of the 20th century boiler shops in every railway works would have had standard systematic repair programmes instead of the foreman's notebook. Unfortunately, railways in Britain tended to be hidebound by long-standing custom and bitter opposition to change almost up to the end of the steam era, and the ways of the Ashford works in 1944 seem to have been those that the SER devised a hundred years earlier.

There was, however, something else. No 1572's boiler had been checked by a boiler inspector no less than nine times after the 1944 general repair; on every occasion this inspector failed to detect the roof stays' corroded state. The only way in which he could have seen these stays was by peeping through any of seven 1½ in holes that normally carried tapered washout plugs, using the usual paraffin-soaked rag on a wire for illumination. At the best he could have seen only a few of the outermost stays, but had he looked he would surely have seen that at least one was heavily rusted away, which ought then to have aroused suspicions about the rest. The managers of preserved railways where steam locomotives are run should never forget the vital importance of checking the roof stays, particularly when they are difficult to inspect.

Lamington, in Scotland, was the scene of the next boiler explosion, the first to occur after the formation of British Railways, and the pathetic events that led up to it make a melancholy tale. The engine involved was the splendid LMS Stanier Coronation 4–6–2 No 46224 *Princess Alexandra*; it was the third of the three engines known to have been involved twice in an explosion, its boiler having had a similar accident in 1940. It had worked about 40 miles with the 9.25pm Glasgow to London passenger train on 7 March 1948 and at 10.44pm was near Lamington station when the firebox crown sheet gave way. The plate did not split, but it had

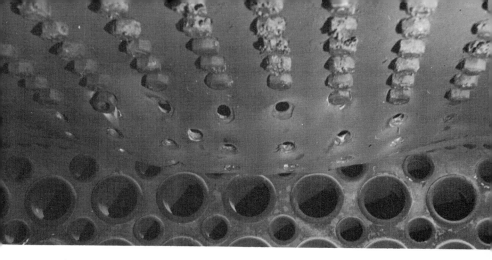

The front of the firebox crown, on LMS Coronation 4–6–2 No 46224, forced down off its roof stays by the explosion at Lamington on 7 March 1948. (*British Railways*)

become so hot and soft due to shortage of water that it was forced over 21 riveted stay heads, pulling the nuts off three others; a tremendous discharge of steam at 240 lb/sq in through the 24 stay holes blew flames through the firehole into the cab. Both enginemen received terrible scalds and burns that in the driver's case were fatal.

The accident happened because the engine was working in a condition when it should not even have been in steam — both the boiler water gauges were defective. These gauges were of a type that had been adopted by the LMSR, despite there being much to be said against the design. Whereas on the gauge that had been standard for at least a century the plug cocks controlling the upper and lower portways into the boiler had handles that lay across the passages when the cocks were open, pointing straight up or straight down, and were in line with them when closed, the LMS gauge had only one handle, on the upper cock, that stood upwards at a 45° angle when the cock was open and downwards at a similar angle when shut. The lower cock's plug had an arm instead of a handle, a rod with forked ends joining it to the handle on the other cock so that both cocks worked simultaneously; both handle and arm fitted onto squares at the ends of their cock plugs. The handle was much longer than those on ordinary plug cocks, on the principle that should the gauge glass burst, a man could pull down the handle and so close both cocks at once without the risk of scalding his hand or cutting it on the broken glass tube. The design did not permit of the portways being tested separately when the engine was in steam, which was a grave disadvantage.

Now for the accident's gloomy story. Three days earlier a fitter at Polmadie shed, Glasgow, fitted a new glass in the right-hand gauge — the engine did not work again until the day before the accident. It was about to take the 9.25pm train from Glasgow as far as Carlisle when the driver noticed that the right-hand gauge glass, towards the fireman's side, was full of water, whereas the other glass was only half filled. He tried to test the right-hand gauge by pulling down its handle, intending to drain it and then refill it by pushing the handle up, but he was unable to expel the water from the glass. Then the driver discovered that all was not well with the left-hand gauge; he drained the glass but it took an unusually long time to refill. At Carlisle he summoned a fitter who concluded when he could not get the right-hand gauge to empty that the boiler was overfilled with water and that the gauge was in order. At the same time the fitter warned another driver who was to work the engine back to Glasgow that the left-hand gauge was not reliable.

This driver reported on reaching Polmadie at about noon on the day of the accident that both gauges needed attention. At 2.00pm a leading fitter examined them and discovered the same discrepancies that the drivers had found but did not do anything beyond telling a fitter to 'make as good a job of it as he could' and then leaving him. A few hours later a driver who was preparing the engine for the Carlisle journey reported the state of the gauges. The leading fitter came back but concentrated on the left-hand gauge in which the water was not standing as high as in the other. Believing the right-hand gauge to be in order and the left-hand gauge at fault, he directed a fitter to renew the left-hand gauge glass and then to test the gauge portways. When the fitter, left on his own, found that the gauge was no better with a new glass, he concluded somewhat impulsively that its handle and arm were on the wrong squares; he pulled the handle down, believing that he was opening the plug cocks, and told the train driver and his fireman why he had done so. He had in fact closed the cocks and had put the gauge out of action.

The fireman tried the left-hand drain cock. This emptied the gauge glass, and when the glass did not refill he regarded the gauge as out of use and relied entirely on the right-hand gauge, at his side of the footplate. The train left Glasgow at 9.25pm but had gone only 8½ miles when the enginemen heard steam escaping and on reaching Carstairs, 29 miles from Glasgow, they summoned a foreman and two fitters from the adjacent running shed. These men made examinations but could not find the cause of the steam leak. As the right-hand glass was full it did not occur to them or the enginemen that the lead in one or both of the firebox's fusible plugs had melted, which is doubtless what had happened. Although fusible plugs are intended as alarms, steam escaping through a plug into a large engine's firebox would be virtually invisible in the fire's glow and heat, and would be drawn towards the tubes by the draught. The train was allowed to continue on its way, only to come to grief at Lamington.

The left-hand gauge had it been in order would have shown the boiler's true water level; it was slow in filling because the forked rod connecting the handle and the arm was too short, so that when the upper cock was open the lower cock was only partly so. The fault caused by this error seems to have attracted everyone's attention, a far more serious defect in the right-hand gauge going undetected. This gauge's handle had been wrongly positioned on the upper plug's square. The fitter who renewed the gauge glass on 4 March appears to have inadvertently re-assembled the equipment in this way but the mistake kept the upper cock closed when the cock below was open, causing the water to rise in the glass well above the level in the boiler, and it was this defect that misled the driver and fireman. The leading fitter could have discovered the fault quickly had he removed the forked rod and tested the gauge by opening the cocks one at a time as on the older type of gauge. Had the gauges been of the older type with independent cocks the wrong assembly could not have occurred, and

Bottom left The firebox outer casing of LBSC E4 0–6–2T No 2557, after removal of the inner copper firebox, showing the corroded right-hand stays which initiated the boiler explosion at Bevois Park, Southampton, on 6 April 1949. (*British Railways*)

Top left No 2557's copper firebox right-hand side bulged in by the explosion at Bevois Park. The steam escaped through 52 stay holes when the plate was pulled off the stays; had the plate burst the boiler would certainly have been destroyed. Note the foundation ring at the base of the firebox. (*British Railways*)

Bottom right View up into the firebox, lying on its side, showing the bulged right-hand plates of No 2557. (*British Railways*)

Top right The outer wrapper of the firebox of SR No 2557 showing the outward bulge after the stays parted. (*British Railways*) the slow filling of the left-hand gauge would have been avoided. On the whole, the suitability of the LMS design was most questionable.

Mr Moore took evidence from about 40 witnesses. His report on the accident was very comprehensive and probably the best ever written on a boiler explosion. The leading fitter who let the engine work when its water gauges were defective received most of the blame but was he, one might ask, under such pressure from higher levels that he withdrew engines from service at his peril? Great stress was being laid at this period on engine availability and shedmasters were judged by their ability to keep engines off the 'stopped list', a policy that led to a good deal of faking and falsifying of the returns on which engines set aside for repairs were listed. There was thus considerable pressure on leading fitters and chargehands to avoid laying-up engines, but to keep them in good order nevertheless. The leading fitter at Polmadie could have called his foreman or even the shedmaster to *Princess Alexandra* instead of leaving a fitter to cope with the mystery. A defective water gauge on any boiler in steam sets up a very grave situation indeed.

1949 and back to the 'Southern', or Southern Region of BR as by then it had become. Bevois Park sidings at Southampton provided the scene for an explosion on 6 April. At 8.05pm the firebox of Class E4 0–6–2 inside-cylinder tank engine No 2557, of LB&SCR origin, burst inwards.

The two enginemen were blown out of the cab by the force of the steam through the firehole and were picked-up severely scalded — fortunately both recovered. When the steam clouds had subsided it was found that the firebox's right-hand side had given way; 137 of the 207 copper stays normally supporting it had broken, allowing the steam pressure to bulge the copper side plate into the firebox and force it off the heads of 52 other stays. The plate was not rent, but steam and water escaped through its 52 open stay holes with explosive force.

The copper stays were found to be badly corroded, some being so reduced in the water space that only a sixth of the original sectional area was left. About 15 of the thinnest stays, in a group, parted first, the additional strain that was then passed to the others breaking them in turn. The stays on the firebox's other side remained intact although they were corroded almost as badly.

After general repairs six years earlier the engine had been based at Horsham until moved to the Southampton area three weeks before the explosion. Locomotive water taken at Horsham came mostly from a borehole, and with a considerable sodium carbonate content it corroded copper at an alarming rate. Only a month before the accident the boiler of No 2557 had been examined by a boiler inspector. He observed that some of the side stays were being attacked by corrosion but declared the boiler to be fit for a further six months' service. Knowing the effects of Horsham water on copper plates and stays, and that the engine had run over 90,000 miles since last in the works, his decision was unfortunate. He should have ordered the engine into works immediately, but he too may have been hesitant to disturb that graven image of the running sheds called *availability*. Six years between general repairs was in any case much too long for any boiler on an engine that worked on arduous service almost daily.

There were no more explosions until 22 December 1952, when at Wheatsheaf Junction in Wales on the Western Region of BR, another firebox crown sheet gave way. A defective water gauge had led to a shortage of water in the same manner but not for the same reason as at Lamington.

Wheatsheaf Junction gave access to a short colliery branch and was about a mile and a half to the north of Wrexham. The engine was 4–6–0 No 6859 *Yiewsley Grange*. The boiler which worked at 225 lb/sq in had only one water gauge, which had one vertical glass tube of the usual form and another (also vertical) but of brass and carrying two test cocks. The glass tube was secured in the normal manner by glands in upper and lower gauge mountings. Each gland was rendered steam-tight by a rubber packing ring that fitted firmly over the glass tube and was squeezed tight by the gland nut. As in the case of *Princess Alexandra* the cocks in the mountings were linked.

No 6859, its boiler in good order, was working the 8.20pm

goods train from Birkenhead to London. Travelling south-wards, it had almost reached Wheatsheaf Junction when the explosion occurred with a report loud enough to be heard by the signalman and by people in houses nearby. The front of the firebox crown sheet had been made red hot by the heat of the fire as the engine worked heavily up a long 1 in 80 gradient and had split along its centre, leaving a 30 in gap nearly 4 in across. The gauge glass had been showing a false high water level, misleading the enginemen. The driver escaped unhurt while the fireman, although badly burned and scalded, recovered in due course. It is remarkable that these two men were not far more gravely injured.

The gauge glass had been inserted four days earlier at Birkenhead, when the engine was not in steam, by an apprentice fitter who had very nearly completed his five years' tutelage. He did not know that the glands on the upper and lower gauge cocks were slightly out of alignment, and remained unaware that as he tightened the upper gland nut he was putting a heavy strain on the glass tube, which snapped within the gland either as he applied his spanner or when the engine was steamed. He appears to have tightened the nut a little harder than was usually the case and its pressure began to squeeze the packing ring between the two pieces of the broken tube, and during the next two days the rubber went further into the gap until the top of the tube was practically closed by it; this obstruction caused the water in the glass to rise higher than the level in the boiler.

On 20 December a driver reported at Oxley, Wolver-hampton, that after No 6859's gauge had been drained the water rose somewhat sluggishly in the glass, but a fitter who was called considered the defect to be so slight that the engine could continue to work. Had he uncoupled the rod that linked the cocks and then tested each cock in turn he would probably have found the defect. The engine returned to Birkenhead, and when the driver of the 8.20pm goods train took charge he observed that the gauge glass was full and assumed that the boiler water level was somewhere in or above the upper gland nut. He or his fireman ought to have tried the two test cocks, as required by Western Region instructions, but neither of them did so and thus remained unaware that the gauge was deceiving them. Shortly before the accident the sound of escaping steam within the firebox attracted their attention but they assumed that a flue tube was punctured. They anticipated that they could at least get to Wrexham and never suspected the truth, which was that the front fusible plug had melted.

After investigation by Mr Moore most of the blame for the accident was laid on the fitting staff for not examining the gauge far more thoroughly than they did. But the value of having upper and lower cocks united by a rod was once again very dubious.

Nine years and a month elapsed before another boiler explosion occurred and it was the last on BR — by then steam locomotives were rapidly dwindling in numbers. On 24 January 1962 the 7.30am Holyhead to London express nearing Bletchley when there was a terrible bang on the engine footplate and high-temperature steam filled the cab; both footplate men were scalded but the driver was able to stop the train. The engine was another Coronation 4–6–2 No 46238 *City of Carlisle*. Water shortage in the boiler was the cause of the explosion, which by good fortune was a very mild one. Although all three lead plugs had fused, the damage amounted only to three downward bulges in the crown sheet and a slight warping of the firebox tubeplate. The crown had become sufficiently hot and plastic for the steam to force it over seven roof stay nuts, leaving holes that permitted the escape of the steam at 250 lb/sq in pressure. It was thanks to the boiler's sound design and excellent condition that the firebox and engine's rear end were not blown to pieces.

Mr E.G. Brown, an employment inspector, held an inquiry and found that the boiler and its fittings were in good order, except for two features. One was that the right-hand gauge glass on the fireman's side of the footplate was so dirty that the water level could not be seen properly, the fireman having used the other gauge to guide him. This glass appeared to be full every time the fireman looked at it during the journey as he could not see the top of the water. In fact it was empty and, unappreciated by the fireman, the water level fell steadily until the crown sheet was high and dry. Neither gauge was fitted with a striped backplate. It had been LNER practice many years for every water gauge back plate to be painted with diagonal black and white lines; when seen through a glass containing water these lines appeared to slope the opposite way and there was no difficulty in telling at a glance whether the glass was full or empty. *City of Carlisle*'s gauges did not possess backplates with such markings — with them, the fireman would not have made his mistake. Was the LMSR and later the London Midland Region too proud to adopt an LNER idea, one wonders?

And so ends the story of boiler explosions. As has been said in the first chapter, hardly a British railway of any size escaped at least one of these accidents, although Ireland appears to have been more fortunate. The company with the worst record was the North Eastern Railway or its earlier constituents, 29 of the total of 137 explosions have occurred on that system, and 18 out of the 29 having occurred during Edward Fletcher's term of office.

It remains a mystery why, throughout the whole of the long era of steam motive power in the British Isles, engine drivers were never given a positive indication by way of a mark or indicator on their water gauges where in the glass their water levels should be maintained and what allowances were needed when their engines were on gradients. Everything that a driver required to know was given to him — boiler pressure, steam heating pressure, Westinghouse air pressure, degrees of vacuum, water tank contents, running times, speed limits and line gradients — everything except the amount of water he should maintain in his boiler. Nowhere was there any information to be had about the depth of water on a boiler's crown sheet when the water stood level with the top of the gauge glass tube's lower nut; that was a secret that never left the locomotive drawing offices. So drivers, along with the men who raised steam for them, were left to decide their water levels for themselves; usually they worked with the water within an inch or so of the upper gland nut. It is very much to their credit that they almost invariably managed their engines with complete success in such circumstances.

Number of steam locomotives owned by railway companies in the British Isles

Year	England & Wales	Scotland	Ireland	TOTAL
1860	4,696	781	324	5,801
1865	5,968	1,026	420	7,414
1870	7,671	1,241	467	9,379
1875	10,434	1,468	537	12,439
1880	11,172	1,618	594	13,384
1885	12,840	1,718	638	15,196
1890	13,731	1,814	692	16,237
1895	15,901	1,986	771	18,658
1900	18,040	2,345	765	21,150
1905	18,881	2,399	876	22,156
1910	19,252	2,495	893	22,640

Index